THE LONE SANE MAN . . .

"You're going on a little trip. It may not be fun, but it'll be interesting."

"Trip? Where to?"

"Sealed orders," said Renn, rather sharply. "You'll be put aboard the latest and best equipped ship that the league can furnish. Your job is to tend the control machinery, and to act as assistant astrogator no matter what happens. You are to obey orders without question, and without the use of force where possible."

"That's all written up, just about word for word, in the Naval Manual. Is there anything special about this voyage that calls for all this underlining?"

"There is definitely something special about this ship. The rest of the crew—it is only fair to tell you—is insane . . ."

CAVIAR

Theodore Sturgeon

A Del Rey Book

BALLANTINE BOOKS • NEW YORK

A Del Rey Book
Published by Ballantine Books

Copyright © 1955 by Theodore Sturgeon

All rights reserved under International and Pan-American
Copyright Conventions. Published in the United States by
Ballantine Books, a division of Random House, Inc., New
York, and simultaneously in Canada by Ballantine Books of
Canada, Ltd., Toronto, Canada.

ACKNOWLEDGMENTS:
"Microcosmic God" appeared in *Astounding Science-Fiction*,
Copyright 1941 by Street & Smith Publications, Inc., also in
WITHOUT SORCERY, Copyright 1948 by Prime Press;
"Medusa" and "Prodigy" appeared in *Astounding Science Fiction*, Copyright 1942 and 1949 respectively by Street & Smith
Publications, Inc.; "Ghost of a Chance" appeared in *Unknown
Worlds* under the title "The Green-Eyed Monster," Copyright
1943 by Street & Smith Publications, Inc., and in *Suspense*,
Spring 1951; "Blabbermouth" appeared in *Amazing Stories*,
Copyright 1945 by Ziff-Davis Publishing Company; "Shadow,
Shadow on the Wall" appeared in *Imagination*, Copyright
1950 by Greenleaf Publishing Company; "Twink" appeared in
Galaxy Science Fiction, Copyright 1955 by Galaxy Publishing
Corporation.

Library of Congress Catalog Card Number: 55-12088

ISBN 0-345-25783-9-150

Manufactured in the United States of America

First Edition: November 1955
Fourth Printing: April 1977

Cover art by Darrell Sweet

Contents

CAVIAR

BRIGHT SEGMENT

HE HAD never held a girl before. He was not terrified; he had used that up earlier when he had carried her in and kicked the door shut behind him and had heard the steady drip of blood from her soaked skirt, and before that, when he had thought her dead there on the curb, and again when she made that sound, that sigh or whispered moan. He had brought her in and when he saw all that blood he had turned left, turned right, put her down on the floor, his brains all clabbered and churned and his temples athump with the unaccustomed exercise. All he could act on was *Don't get blood on the bedspread*. He turned on the overhead light and stood for a moment blinking and breathing hard; suddenly he leaped for the window to lower the blind against the street light staring in and all other eyes. He saw his hands reach for the blind and checked himself; they were red and ready to paint anything he touched. He made a sound, a detached part of his mind recognizing it as the exact duplicate of that agonized whisper she had uttered out there on the dark, wet street, and leapt to the light switch, seeing the one red smudge already there, knowing as he swept his hand over it he was leaving another. He stumbled to the sink in the corner and washed his hands, washed them again, every few seconds looking over his shoulder at the girl's body and the thick flat finger of blood which crept curling toward him over the linoleum.

He had his breath now, and moved more carefully to the window. He drew down the blind and pulled the curtains and looked at the sides and the bottom to see that there were no crevices. In pitch blackness he felt his way back to the opposite wall, going around the

2

edges of the linoleum, and turned on the light again. The finger of blood was a tentacle now, fumbling toward the soft, stain-starved floorboards. From the enamel table beside the stove he snatched a plastic sponge and dropped it on the tentacle's seeking tip and was pleased, it was a reaching thing no more, it was only something spilled that could be mopped up.

He took off the bedspread and hung it over the brass headrail. From the drawer of the china closet and from the gate leg table he took his two plastic table cloths. He covered the bed with them, leaving plenty of overlap, then stood a moment rocking with worry and pulling out his lower lip with a thumb and forefinger. *Fix it right,* he told himself firmly. So she'll die before you fix it, never mind, fix it, right.

He expelled air from his nostrils and got books from the shelf in the china closet—a six-year-old World Almanac, a half-dozen paperbacked novels, a heavy catalog of jewelry findings. He pulled the bed away from the wall and put books one by one under two of the legs so that the bed was tilted slightly down to the foot and slightly to one side. He got a blanket and rolled it and slipped it under the plastic so that it formed a sort of fence down the high side. He got a six-quart aluminum pot from under the sink and set it on the floor by the lowest corner of the bed and pushed the trailing end of plastic down into it. *So bleed now,* he told the girl silently, with satisfaction.

He bent over her and grunted, lifting her by the armpits. Her head fell back as if she had no bones in her neck and he almost dropped her. He dragged her to the bed, leaving a wide red swath as her skirt trailed through the scarlet puddle she had lain in. He lifted her clear of the floor, settled his feet, and leaned over the bed with her in his arms. It took an unexpected effort to do it. He realized only then how drained, how tired he was, and how old. He put her down clumsily, almost dropping her in an effort to leave the carefully arranged tablecloths undisturbed, and he very nearly fell into the bed with her. He levered himself away with rubbery arms and stood panting. Around the soggy hem of her skirt blood began to gather, and as he watched, began to find its way lazily to the low corner. *So much, so much blood in a person,* he marveled, and *stop it, how to make it stop if it won't stop?*

He glanced at the locked door, the blinded window, the clock. He listened. It was raining harder now, drumming and hissing in the darkest hours. Otherwise nothing; the house was asleep and the street, dead. He was alone with his problem.

He pulled at his lip, then snatched his hand away as he tasted her blood. He coughed and ran to the sink and spat, and washed his mouth and then his hands.

So all right, go call up. . . .

Call up? Call what, the hospital they should call the cops? Might as well call the cops altogether. *Stupid.* What could I tell them, she's my sister, she's hit by a car, they going to believe me? Tell them the truth, a block away I see somebody push her out of a car, drive off, no lights, I bring her in out of the rain, only inside I find she is bleeding like this, they believe me? *Stupid.* What's the matter with you, mind your own business why don't you.

He thought he would pick her up now and put her back in the rain. Yes and somebody sees you, *stupid.*

He saw that the wide, streaked patch of blood on the linoleum was losing gloss where it lay thin, drying and soaking in. He picked up the sponge, two-thirds red now and the rest its original baby-blue except at one end where it looked like bread drawn with a sharp red pencil. He turned it over so it wouldn't drip while he carried it and took it to the sink and rinsed it, wringing it over and over in the running water. *Stupid,* call up somebody and get help.

Call who?

He thought of the department store where for eighteen years he had waxed floors and vacuumed rugs at night. The neighborhood, where he knew the grocery and the butcher. Closed up, asleep, everybody gone; names, numbers he didn't know and anyway, who to trust? *My God in fifty-three years you haven't got a friend?*

He took the clean sponge and sank to his knees on the linoleum, and just then the band of blood creeping down the bed reached the corner and turned to a sharp streak; *ponk* it went into the pan, and *pitti-pittipitti* in a rush, then drip-drip-drip-drip, three to the second and not stopping. He knew then with absolute and belated certainty that this bleeding was not going to stop by itself. He whimpered softly and then got up and went to the bed. *"Don't be dead,"* he said aloud, and the way his voice sounded, it frightened him. He put out his hand to her chest, but drew it back when he saw her blouse was torn and blood came from there too.

He swallowed hard and then began fumbling with her clothes. Flat ballet slippers, worn, soggy, thin like paper and little silken things he had never seen before, like just the foot of a stocking. More blood on—but no, that was peeled and chipped enamel on her cold white toes. The skirt had a button at the side and a zipper which baffled him for a moment, but he got it down and tugged the skirt off in an interminable series of jerks from the hem, one side and the other, while she rolled slightly and limply to the motion. Small silken pants, completely soaked and so badly cut on the left side that he snapped them apart easily between his fingers; but the other side was surprisingly strong and he had to get his scissors to cut them away. The blouse buttoned up the front and was no problem; under it was a brassiere which was cut right in two near the front. He lifted it away but had to cut one of the straps with his scissors to free it altogether.

He ran to the sink with his sponge, washed it and wrung it out, filled a saucepan with warm water and ran back. He sponged the body down; it looked firm but too thin, with its shadow-ladder of ribs down each side and the sharp protrusion of the hip-bones. Under the left breast was a long cut, starting on the ribs in front and curving upward almost to the nipple. It seemed deep but the blood merely welled out. The other cut, though, in her groin, released blood brightly in regular gouts, one after the other, eager but weakly. He had seen the like before, the time Garber pinched his arm off in the elevator cable-room, but then the blood squirted a foot away. Maybe this did, too, he thought suddenly, but now it's slowing up, now it's go-

ing to stop, yes, and you, stupid, you have a dead body
you can tell stories to the police.

He wrung out the sponge in the water and mopped
the wound. Before it could fill up again he spread the
sides of the cut and looked down into it. He could
clearly see the femoral artery, looking like an end of
spaghetti and cut almost through; and then there was
nothing but blood again.

He squatted back on his heels, pulling heedlessly at
his lip with his bloody hand and trying to think. *Pinch,
shut, squeeze. Squeezers. Tweezers!* He ran to his tool-
box and clawed it open. Years ago he had learned to
make fine chains out of square silver wire, and he used
to pass the time away by making link after tiny link,
soldering each one closed with an alcohol torch and a
needle-tipped iron. He picked up the tweezers and
dropped them in favor of the small spring clamp which
he used for holding the link while he worked on it. He
ran to the sink and washed the clamp and came back
to the bed. Again he sponged away the little lake of
blood, and quickly reached down and got the fine jaws
of the clamp on the artery near its cut. Immediately
there was another gush of blood. Again he sponged it
away, and in a blaze of inspiration, released the clamp,
moved it to the other side of the cut, and clamped it
again.

Blood still oozed from the inside of the wound, but
that terrible pulsing gush was gone. He sat back on his
heels and painfully released a breath he must have
held for two minutes. His eyes ached from the strain,
and his brain was still whirling, but with these was a
feeling, a new feeling almost like an ache or a pain,
but it was nowhere and everywhere inside him; it
wanted him to laugh but at the same time his eyes
stung and hot salt squeezed out through holes too small
for it.

After a time he recovered, blinking away his ex-
haustion, and sprang up, overwhelmed by urgency.
Got to fix everything. He went to the medicine cabinet
over the sink. Adhesive tape, pack of gauze pads.
Maybe not big enough; okay tape together, fix right.
New tube this sulfa-thia-dia-whatchamacall-um, fix

anything, time I got vacuum-cleaner grit in cut hand, infection. Fixed boils too.

He filled a kettle and his saucepan with clean water and put them on the stove. Sew up, yes. He found needles, white thread, dumped them into the water. He went back to the bed and stood musing for a long time, looking at the oozing gash under the girl's breast. He sponged out the femoral wound again and stared pensively into it until the blood slowly covered the clamped artery. He could not be positive, but he had a vague recollection of something about tourniquets, they should be opened up every once in a while or there is trouble; same for an artery, maybe? Better he should sew up the artery; it was only opened, not cut through. If he could find out how to do it and still let it be like a pipe, not like a darned sock.

So into the pot went the tweezers, a small pair of needle-nose pliers, and, after some more thought, a dozen silver broach-pins out of his jewelry kit. Waiting for the water to boil, he inspected the wounds again. He pulled on his lip, frowning, then got another fine needle, held it with pliers in the gas flame until it was red, and with another of his set of pliers bent it around in a small semi-circle and dropped it into the water. From the sponge he cut a number of small flat slabs and dropped them in too.

He glanced at the clock, and then for ten minutes he scrubbed the white enamel table-top with cleanser. He tipped it into the sink, rinsed it at the faucet, and then slowly poured the contents of the kettle over it. He took it to the stove, held it with one hand while he fished in the boiling saucepan with a silver knife until he had the pliers resting with their handles out of the water. He grasped them gingerly with a clean wash-cloth and carefully, one by one, transferred everything from saucepan to table. By the time he had found the last of the needles and the elusive silver pins, sweat was running into his eyes and the arm that held the table-top threatened to drop right off. But he set his stumpy yellow teeth and kept at it.

Carrying the table-top, he kicked a wooden chair bit by bit across the room until it rested by the bed, and set his burden down on its seat. *This no hospital,* he thought, *but I fix everything.*

Hospital! Yes, in the movies—

He went to a drawer and got a clean white handkerchief and tried to tie it over his mouth and nose like in the movies. His knobby face and square head were too much for one handkerchief; it took three before he got it right, with a great white tassel hanging down the back like in an airplane picture.

He looked helplessly at his hands, then shrugged; so no rubber globes, what the hell. I wash good. His hands were already pink and wrinkled from his labors, but he went back to the sink and scratched a bar of soap until his horny nails were packed with it, then cleaned them with a file until they hurt, and washed and cleaned them again. And at last he knelt by the bed, holding his shriven hands up in a careful salaam. Almost, he reached for his lip to pull it, but not quite.

He squeezed out two globs of the sulfa ointment onto the table top and, with the pliers, squashed two slabs of sponge until the creamy stuff was through and through them. He mopped out the femoral wound and placed a medicated sponge on each side of the wound, leaving the artery exposed at the bottom. Using tweezers and pliers, he laboriously threaded the curved needle while quelling the urge to stick the end of the thread into his mouth.

He managed to get four tiny stitches into the artery below the break, out of it above the break. Each one he knotted with exquisite care so that the thread would not cut the tissue but still would draw the severed edges together. Then he squatted back on his heels to rest, his shoulders afire with tension, his eyes misted. Then, taking a deep breath, he removed the clamp.

Blood filled the wound and soaked the sponges. But it came slowly, without spurting. He shrugged grimly. So what's to do, use a tire patch? He mopped the blood out once more, and quickly filled the incision with ointment, slapping a piece of gauze over it more to hide it than to help it.

He wiped his eyebrows first with one shoulder, then the other, and fixed his eyes on the opposite wall the way he used to do when he worked on his little silver chains. When the mist went away he turned his attention to the long cut on the underside of the breast. He didn't know how to stitch one this size, but he could cook and he knew how to skewer up a chicken. Biting his tongue, he stuck the first of his silver pins into the flesh at right angles to the cut, pressing it across the wound and out the other side. He started the next pin not quite an inch away, and the same with the third. The fourth grated on something in the wound; it startled him like a door slamming and he bit his tongue painfully. He backed the pin out and probed carefully with his tweezers. Yes, something hard in there. He probed deeper with both points of the tweezers, feeling them enter uncut tissue with a soft crunching that only a fearful fingertip could hear. He conquered a shudder and glanced up at the girl's face. He resolved not to look up there again. It was a very dead face.

Stupid! but the self-insult was lost in concentration even as it was born. The tweezers closed on something hard, slippery and stubborn. He worked it gently back and forth, feeling a puzzled annoyance at this unfamiliar flesh that yielded as he moved. Gradually, very gradually, a sharp angular corner of *something* appeared. He kept at it until there was enough to grasp with his fingers; then he set his tweezers aside and gently worked it loose. Blood began to flow freely before it was half out, but he did not stop until he could draw it free. The light glinted on the strip of hollow-ground steel and its shattered margins; he turned it over twice before it came to him that it was a piece of straight razor. He set it down on his enamel table, thinking of what the police might have said to him if he had turned her over to them with that story about a car accident.

He stanched the blood, pulled the wound as wide apart as he could. The nipple writhed under his fingers, its pink halo shrunken and wrinkled; he grunted, thinking that a bug had crawled under his hand, and then aware that whatever the thing meant, it couldn't mean death, not yet anyway. He had to go back and start over, stanching the cut and spreading it, and quickly squeezing in as much ointment as it would hold. Then he went on with his insertion of the silver pins, until there was a little ladder of twelve of them from one end of the wound to the other. He took his thread, doubled it, put the loop around the topmost pin and drew the two parts of the thread underneath. Holding them both in one hand, he gently pinched the edges of the wound together at the pin. Then he drew the loop tight without cutting, crossed the threads and put them under the next pin, and again closed the wound. He continued this all the way down, lacing the cut closed around the ladder of pins. At the bottom he tied the thread off and cut it. There was blood and ointment all over his handiwork, but when he mopped up it looked good to him.

He stood up and let sensation flow agonizingly into his numb feet. He was sopping wet; he could feel perspiration searching its way down through the hairs of his legs; like a migration of bedbugs. He looked down at himself; wrinkles and water and blood. He looked across at the wavery mirror, and saw a bandaged goblin with brow-ridges like a shelf and sunken eyes with a cast to them, with grizzled hair which could be scrubbed only to the color of grime, and with a great gout of blood where the mouth hid behind the bandage. He snatched it down and looked again. *More better you cover your face, no matter what.* He turned away, not from his face, but with it, in the pained patience of a burro with saddle sores.

Wearily he carried his enameled table-top to the sink. He washed his hands and forearms and took off the handkerchiefs from around his neck and washed his face. Then he got what was left of his sponge and a pan of warm soapy water and came back to the bed.

It took him hours. He sponged the tablecloths on which she lay, shifted her gently so as to put no strain on the wounds, and washed and dried where she had lain. He washed her from head to toe, going back for clean water, and then had to dry the bed again afterward. When he lifted her head he found her hair matted and tacky with rain and drying blood, and fresh blood with it, so he propped up her shoulders with a

big pillow under the plastic and tipped her head back
and washed and dried her hair, and found an ugly lump
and a bleeding contusion on the back of her head. He
combed the hair away from it on each side and put
cold water on it, and it stopped bleeding, but there was
a lump the size of a plum. He separated half a dozen
of the gauze pads and packed them around the lump
so that it need not take the pressure off her head; he
dared not turn her over.

When her hair was wet and fouled it was only a dark
mat, but cleaned and combed, it was the darkest of
auburns, perfectly straight. There was a broad lustrous
band of it on the bed on each side of her face, which
was radiant with pallor, cold as a moon. He covered
her with the bedspread, and for a long while stood over
her, full of that strange nowhere-everywhere almost-
pain, not liking it but afraid to turn away from it . . .
maybe he would never have it again.

He sighed, a thing that came from his marrow and
his years, and doggedly set to work scrubbing the floor.
When he had finished, and the needles and thread were
put away, the bit of tape which he had not used, the
wrappers of the gauze pads and the pan of blood from
the end of the bed disposed of, and all the tools cleaned
and back in their box, the night was over and daylight
pressed weakly against the drawn blind. He turned
out the light and stood without breathing, listening with
all his mind, wanting to know from where he stood if
she still lived. To bend close and find out she was gone
—oh no. He wanted to know from here.

But a truck went by, and a woman called a child,
and someone laughed; so he went and knelt by the bed
and closed his eyes and slowly put his hand on her
throat. It was cool—please, not cold!—and quiet as a
lost glove.

Then the hairs on the back of his hand stirred to her
breath, and again, the faintest of motions. The stinging
came to his eyes and through and through him came
the fiery urge to *do*: make some soup, buy some medicine, maybe, for her, a ribbon or a watch; clean the
house, run to the store . . . and while doing all these
things, all at once, to shout and shout great shaking

wordless bellows to tell himself over and over again, so he could hear for sure, that she was alive. At the very peak of this explosion of urges, there was a funny little side-slip and he was fast asleep.

He dreamed someone was sewing his legs together with a big curved sail needle, and at the same time drawing the thread from his belly; he could feel the spool inside spinning and emptying. He groaned and opened his eyes, and knew instantly where he was and what had happened, and hated himself for the noise he made. He lifted his hand and churned his fingers to be sure they could feel, and lowered them gently to her throat. It was warm—no, hot, too hot. He pushed back from the bed and scrabbled half-across the floor on his knuckles and his numb, rubbery legs. Cursing silently he made a long lunge and caught the wooden chair to him, and used it to climb to his feet. He dared not let it go, so clumped softly with it over to the corner, where he twisted and hung gasping to the edge of the sink, while boiling acid ate downward through his legs. When he could, he splashed cold water on his face and neck and, still drying himself on a towel, stumbled across to the bed. He flung the bedspread off and *stupid!* he almost screamed as it plucked at his fingers on the way; it had adhered to the wound in her groin and he was sure he had ripped it to shreds, torn a whole section out of the clumsily patched artery. And he couldn't see; it must be getting dark outside; how long had he crouched there? He ran to the light switch, leaped back. Yes, bleeding, it was bleeding again—

But a little, only a very little. The gauze was turned up perhaps halfway, and though the exposed wound was wet with blood, blood was not running. It had, while he was asleep, but hardly enough to find its way to the mattress. He lifted the loose corner of the gauze very gently, and found it stuck fast. But the sponges, the little sponges to put on the sulfa-whatchama, they were still in the wound. He'd meant to take them out after a couple of hours, not let the whole clot form around them!

He ran for warm water, his big sponge. Soap in it,

yes. He squatted beside the bed, though his legs still protested noisily, and began to bathe the gauze with tiny, gentle touches.

Something made him look up. She had her eyes open, and was looking down at him. Her face and her eyes were utterly without expression. He watched them close slowly and slowly open again, lackluster and uninterested. "All right, all right," he said harshly, "I fix everything." She just kept on looking. He nodded violently, it was all that soothes, all that encourages, hope for her and a total promise for her, but it was only a rapid bobbing of his big ugly head. Annoyed as he always was at his own speechlessness, he went back to work. He got the gauze off and began soaking the edge of one of the sponges. When he thought it was ready to come, he tugged gently at it.

In a high, whispery soprano, "Ho-o-o-o . . . ?" she said; it was like a question and a sob. Slowly she turned her head to the left. "Ho-o-o-o?" She turned her head again and slipped back to unconsciousness.

"I," he said loudly, excitedly, and "I—" and that was all; she wouldn't hear him anyway. He held still until his hands stopped trembling, and went on with the job.

The wound looked wonderfully clean, though the skin all around it was dry and hot.

Down inside the cut he could see the artery in a nest of wet jelly; that was probably right—he didn't know, but it looked all right, he wouldn't disturb it. He packed the opening full of ointment, pressed the edges gently together, and put on a piece of tape. It promptly came unstuck, so he discarded it and dried the flesh all around the wound, put on gauze first, then the tape, and this time it held.

The other cut was quite closed, though more so where the pins were than between them. It too was surrounded by hot, dry, red flesh.

The scrape on the back of her head had not bled, but the lump was bigger than ever. Her face and neck were dry and very warm, though the rest of her body seemed cool. He went for a cold cloth and put it across her eyes and pressed it down on her cheeks, and she sighed.

When he took it away she was looking at him again. "You all right?" he asked her, and inanely, "You all right," he told her. A small frown flickered for a moment and then her eyes closed. He knew somehow that she was asleep. He touched her cheeks with the backs of his fingers. "Very hot," he muttered.

He turned out the light and in the dimness changed his clothes. From the bottom of a drawer he took a child's exercise book, and from it a piece of paper with a telephone number in large black penciled script. "I come back," he said to the darkness. She didn't say anything. He went out, locking the door behind him.

Laboriously he called the office from the big drugstore, referring to his paper for each digit and for each, holding the dial against the stop for a full three or four seconds as if to be sure the number would stick. He got the big boss Mr. Laddie first of all, which was acutely embarrassing; he had not spoken to him in a dozen years. At the top of his bull voice he collided with Laddie's third impatient "Hello?" with "Sick! I—uh, sick!" He heard the phone say "—in God's name . . . ?" and Mr. Wismer's laughter, and "Gimme the phone, that's got to be that orangutan of mine," and right in his ear, "Hello?"

"Sick tonight," he shouted.

"What's the matter with you?"

He swallowed. "I can't," he yelled.

"That's just old age," said Mr. Wismer. He heard Mr. Laddie laughing too. Mr. Wismer said, "How many nights you had off in the last fifteen years?"

He thought about it. "No!" he roared. Anyway, it was eighteen years.

"You know, that's right," said Mr. Wismer, speaking to Mr. Laddie without trying to cover his phone, "Fifteen years and never asked for a night off before."

"So who needs him? Give him all his nights off."

"Not at those prices," said Mr. Wismer, and to his phone, "Sure, dummy, take off. Don't work no con games." The phone clicked off on laughter, and he waited there in the booth until he was sure nothing else would be said. Then he hung up his receiver and emerged into the big drugstore where everyone all over was looking at him. Well, they always did. That didn't bother him. Only one thing bothered him, and that was Mr. Laddie's voice saying over and over in his head, "So who needs him?" He knew he would have to stop and face those words and let them and all that went with them go through his mind. But not now, please not now.

He kept them away by being busy; he bought tape and gauze and ointment and a canvas cot and three icebags and, after some thought, aspirin, because someone had told him once . . . and then to the supermarket where he bought enough to feed a family of nine for nine days. And for all his bundles, he still had a thick arm and a wide shoulder for a twenty-five-pound cake of ice.

He got the door open and the ice in the box, and went out in the hall and picked up the bundles and brought those in, and then went to her. She was burning up, and her breathing was like the way seabirds fly into the wind, a small beat, a small beat, and a long wait, balancing. He cracked a corner off the ice-cake, wrapped it in a dishtowel and whacked it angrily against the sink. He crowded the crushed ice into one of the bags and put it on her head. She sighed but did not open her eyes. He filled the other bags and put one on her breast and one on her groin. He wrung his hands uselessly over her until it came to him *she has to eat, losing blood like that.*

So he cooked, tremendously, watching her every second minute. He made minestrone and baked cabbage and mashed potatoes and veal cutlets. He cut a pie and warmed cinnamon buns, and he had hot coffee with icecream ready to spoon into it. She didn't eat it, any of it, nor did she drink a drop. She lay there and occasionally let her head fall to the side, so he had to run and pick up the icebag and replace it. Once again she sighed, and once he thought she opened her eyes, but couldn't be sure.

On the second day she ate nothing and drank nothing, and her fever was unbelievable. During the night, crouched on the floor beside her, he awoke once with the echoes of weeping still in the room, but he may have dreamed it.

Once he cut the tenderest, juiciest piece of veal he could find on a cutlet, and put it between her lips. Three hours later he pressed them apart to put in another piece, but the first one was still there. The same thing happened with aspirin, little white crumbs on a dry tongue.

And the time soon came when he had busied himself out of things to do, and fretted himself into a worry-reflex that operated by itself, and the very act of thinking new thoughts trapped him into facing the old ones, and then of course there was nothing to do but let them run on through, with all the ache and humiliation they carried with them. He was trying to think a new thing about what would happen if he called a doctor, and the doctor would want to take her to a hospital; he would say, "She needs treatment, old man, she doesn't need you," and there it was in his mind, ready to run, so:

Be eleven years old, bulky and strong and shy, standing in the kitchen doorway, holding your wooden box by its string and trying to shape your mouth so that the reluctant words can press out properly; and there's Mama hunched over a gin bottle like a cat over a half-eaten bird, peering; watch her lipless wide mouth twitch and say, "Don't stand there clackin' and slurpin'! Speak up, boy! What are you tryin' to say, you're leaving?"

So nod, it's easier, and she'll say "Leave, then, leave, who needs you?" and you go:

And be a squat, powerful sixteen and go to the recruiting station and watch the sergeant with the presses and creases asking "Whadda *you* want?" and you try, you try and you can't say it so you nod your head at the poster with the pointing finger, UNCLE SAM NEEDS YOU; and the sergeant glances at it and at you, and suddenly his pointing finger is half an inch away from your nose; crosseyed you watch it while he barks, "Well, Uncle don't need *you!*" and you wait, watching the finger that way, not moving until you understand; you understand things real good, it's just that you hear slowly. So there you hang crosseyed and they all laugh.

Or 'way back, you're eight years old and in school, that Phyllis with the row of springy brown sausage-curls flying when she tosses her head, pink and clean and so pretty; you have the chocolates wrapped in gold paper tied in gold-string mesh; you go up the aisle to her desk and put the chocolates down and run back; she comes down the aisle and throws them so hard the mesh breaks on your desk and she says, loud, "I don't need these and I don't need you, and you know what, you got snot on your face," and you put up your hand and sure enough you have.

That's all. Only every time anyone says "Who needs him?" or the like, you have to go through all of them, every one. Sooner or later, however much you put it off, you've got to do it all.

I get doctor, you don't need me.

You die, you don't need me.

Please . . .

Far back in her throat, a scraping hiss, and her lips moved. She held his eyes with hers, and her lips moved silently, and a little late for the lips, the hiss came again. He didn't know how he guessed right, but he did and brought water, dribbling it slowly on her mouth. She licked at it greedily, lifting her head up. He put a hand under it, being careful of the lump, and helped her. After a while she slumped back and smiled weakly at the cup. Then she looked up into his face and though the smile disappeared, he felt much better. He ran to the icebox and the stove, and got glasses and straws—one each of orange juice, chocolate milk, plain milk, consommé from a can, and ice water. He lined them up on the chair-seat by the bed and watched them and her eagerly, like a circus seal waiting to play "America" on the bulb-horns. She did smile this time, faintly, briefly, but right at him, and he tried the consommé. She drank almost half of it through the straw without stopping and fell asleep.

Later, when he checked to see if there was any bleeding, the plastic sheet was wet, but not with blood.

Stupid! he raged at himself, and stamped out and bought a bedpan.

She slept a lot now, and ate often but lightly. She began to watch him as he moved about; sometimes when he thought she was asleep, he would turn and meet her eyes. Mostly, it was his hands she watched, those next two days. He washed and ironed her clothes, and sat and mended them with straight small stitches; he hung by his elbows to the edge of the enameled table and worked his silver wire, making her a broach like a flower on a fan, and a pendant on a silver chain, and a bracelet to match them. She watched his hands while he cooked; he made his own spaghetti— tagliatelli, really—rolling and rolling the dough until it was a huge tough sheet, winding it up like a jelly-roll only tight, slicing it in quick, accurate flickers of a paring-knife so it came out like yellow-white flat shoe-laces. He had hands which had never learned their limitations, because he had never thought to limit them. Nothing else in life cared for this man but his hands, and since they did everything, they could do anything.

But when he changed her dressings or washed her, or helped with the bedpan, she never looked at his hands. She would lie perfectly still and watch his face.

She was very weak at first and could move nothing but her head. He was glad because her stitches were healing nicely. When he withdrew the pins it must have hurt, but she made not a sound; twelve flickers of her smooth brow, one for each pin as it came out.

"Hurts," he rumbled.

Faintly, she nodded. It was the first communication between them, except for those mute, crowded eyes following him about. She smiled too, as she nodded, and he turned his back and ground his knuckles into his eyes and felt wonderful.

He went back to work on the sixth night, having puttered and fussed over her all day to keep her from sleeping until he was ready to leave, then not leaving until he was sure she was fast asleep. He would lock her in and hurry to work, warm inside and ready to do three men's work; and home again in the dark early hours as fast as his bandy legs would carry him, bringing her a present—a little radio, a scarf, something special to eat—every single day. He would lock the door firmly and then hurry to her, touching her forehead and cheek to see what her temperature was, straightening the bed gently so she wouldn't wake. Then he would go out of her sight, away back by the sink, and undress and change to the long drawers he slept in, and come back and curl up on the camp cot. For perhaps an hour and a half he would sleep like a stone, but after that the slightest rustle of her sheet, the smallest catch of breath, would bring him to her in a bound, croaking, "You all right?" and hanging over her tensely, frantically trying to divine what she might need, what he might do or get for her.

And when the daylight came he would give her warm milk with an egg beaten in it, and then he would bathe her and change her dressings and comb her hair, and when there was nothing left to do for her he would clean the room, scrub the floor, wash clothes and dishes and, interminably, cook. In the afternoon he shopped, moving everywhere at a half-trot, running home again as soon as he could to show her what he had bought, what he had planned for her dinner. All these days, and then these weeks, he glowed inwardly, hugging the glow while he was away from her, fanning it with her presence when they were together.

He found her crying one afternoon late in the second week, staring at the little radio with the tears streaking her face. He made a harsh cooing syllable and wiped her cheeks with a dry washcloth and stood back with torture on his animal face. She patted his hand weakly, and made a series of faint gestures which utterly baffled him. He sat on the bedside chair and put his face close to hers as if he could tear the meaning out of her with his eyes. There was something different about her; she had watched him, up to now, with the fascinated, uncomprehending attention of a kitten watching a tankful of tropical fish; but now there was something more in her gaze, in the way she moved and in what she did.

"You hurt?" he rasped.

She shook her head. Her mouth moved, and she pointed to it and began to cry again.

"Oh, you hungry. I fix, fix good." He rose but she caught his wrist, shaking her head and crying, but smiling too. He sat down, torn apart by his perplexity. Again she moved her mouth, pointing to it, shaking her head.

"No talk," he said. She was breathing so hard it frightened him, but when he said that she gasped and half sat up; he caught her shoulders and put her down, but she was nodding urgently. "You can't talk!" he said.

Yes, yes! she nodded.

He looked at her for a long time. The music on the radio stopped and someone began to sell used cars in a crackling baritone. She glanced at it and her eyes filled with tears again. He leaned across her and shut the set off. After a profound effort he formed his mouth in the right shape and released a disdainful snort: "Ha! What you want talk? Don't talk. I fix everything, no talk. I—" He ran out of words, so instead slapped himself powerfully on the chest and nodded at her, the stove, the bedpan, the tray of bandages. He said again, "What you want talk?"

She looked up at him, overwhelmed by his violence, and shrank down. He tenderly wiped her cheeks again, mumbling, "I fix everything."

He came home in the dark one morning, and after seeing that she was comfortable according to his iron standards, went to bed. The smell of bacon and fresh coffee was, of course, part of a dream; what else could it be? And the faint sounds of movement around the room had to be his weary imagination.

He opened his eyes on the dream and closed them again, laughing at himself for a crazy stupid. Then he went still inside, and slowly opened his eyes again.

Beside his cot was the bedside chair, and on it was a plate of fried eggs and crisp bacon, a cup of strong black coffee, toast with the gold of butter disappearing into its older gold. He stared at these things in total disbelief, and then looked up.

She was sitting on the end of the bed, where it formed an eight-inch corridor between itself and the cot. She wore her pressed and mended blouse and her skirt. Her shoulders sagged with weariness and she seemed to have some difficulty in holding her head up; her hands hung limply between her knees. But her face was suffused with delight and anticipation as she watched him waking up to his breakfast.

His mouth writhed and he bared his blunt yellow teeth, and ground them together while he uttered a howl of fury. It was a strangled, rasping sound and she scuttled away from it as if it had burned her, and crouched in the middle of the bed with her eyes huge and her mouth slack. He advanced on her with his arms raised and his big fists clenched; she dropped her face on the bed and covered the back of her neck with both hands and lay there trembling. For a long moment he hung over her, then slowly dropped his arms. He tugged at the skirt. "Take off," he grated. He tugged it again, harder.

She peeped up at him and then slowly turned over. She fumbled weakly at the button. He helped her. He pulled the skirt away and tossed it on the cot, and gestured sternly at the blouse. She unbuttoned it and he lifted it from her shoulders. He pulled down the sheet, taking it right out from under her. He took her ankles gently in his powerful hands and pulled them down until she was straightened out on the bed, and then covered her carefully. He was breathing hard. She watched him in terror.

In a frightening quiet he turned back to his cot and the laden chair beside it. Slowly he picked up the cup of coffee and smashed it on the floor. Steadily as the beat of a woodman's axe the saucer followed, the plate of toast, the place of eggs. China and yolk squirted and sprayed over the floor and on the walls. When he had finished he turned back to her. "I fix everything," he said hoarsely. He emphasized each syllable with a thick forefinger as he said again, "*I* fix everything."

She whipped over on her stomach and buried her

face in the pillow, and began to sob so hard he could feel the bed shaking the floor through the soles of his feet. He turned angrily away from her and got a pan and a scrub-brush and a broom and dustpan, and laboriously, methodically, cleaned up the mess.

Two hours later he approached her where she lay, still on her stomach, stiff and motionless. He had had a long time to think of what to say: "Look, you see, you *sick* . . . you see?" He said it, as gently as he could. He put his hand on her shoulder but she twitched violently, flinging it away. Hurt and baffled, he backed away and sat down on the couch, watching her miserably.

She wouldn't eat any lunch.

She wouldn't eat any dinner.

As the time approached for him to go to work, she turned over. He still sat on the cot in his long johns, utter misery on his face and in every line of his ugly body. She looked at him and her eyes filled with tears. He met her gaze but did not move. She sighed suddenly and held out her hand. He leaped to it and pulled it to his forehead, knelt, bowed over it and began to cry. She patted his wiry hair until the storm passed, which it did abruptly, at its height. He sprang away from her and clattered pans on the stove, and in a few minutes brought her some bread and gravy and a parboiled artichoke, rich with olive oil and basil. She smiled wanly and took the plate, and slowly ate while he watched each mouthful and radiated what could only be gratitude. Then he changed his clothes and went to work.

He brought her a red housecoat when she began to sit up, though he would not let her out of bed. He brought her a glass globe in which a flower would keep, submerged in water, for a week, and two live turtles in a plastic bowl and a pale-blue toy rabbit with a music box in it that played "Rock-a-bye Baby" and a blinding vermilion lipstick. She remained obedient and more watchful than ever; when his fussing and puttering were over and he took up his crouch on the cot, waiting for whatever need in her he could divine next, their eyes would meet, and increasingly, his would drop. She would hold the blue rabbit tight to her and watch him unblinkingly, or smile suddenly, parting her lips as if something vitally important and deeply happy was about to escape them. Sometimes she seemed inexpressibly sad, and sometimes she was so restless that he would go to her and stroke her hair until she fell asleep, or seemed to. It occurred to him that he had not seen her wounds for almost two days, and that perhaps they were bothering her during one of these restless spells, and so he pressed her gently down and uncovered her. He touched the scar carefully and she suddenly thrust his hand away and grasped her own flesh firmly, kneading it, slapping it stingingly. Shocked, he looked at her face and saw she was smiling, nodding. "Hurt?" She shook her head. He said, proudly, as he covered her, "I fix. I fix good." She nodded and caught his hand briefly between her chin and her shoulder.

It was that night, after he had fallen into that heavy first sleep on his return from the store, that he felt the warm firm length of her tight up against him on the cot. He lay still for a moment, somnolent, uncomprehending, while quick fingers plucked at the buttons of his long johns. He brought his hands up and trapped her wrists. She was immediately still, though her breath came swiftly and her heart pounded his chest like an angry little knuckle. He made a labored, inquisitive syllable, "Wh-wha . . . ?" and she moved against him and then stopped, trembling. He held her wrists for more than a minute, trying to think this out, and at last sat up. He put one arm around her shoulders and the other under her knees. He stood up. She clung to him and the breath hissed in her nostrils. He moved to the side of her bed and bent slowly and put her down. He had to reach back and detach her arms from around his neck before he could straighten up. "You sleep," he said. He fumbled for the sheet and pulled it over her and tucked it around her. She lay absolutely motionless, and he touched her hair and went back to his cot. He lay down and after a long time fell into a troubled sleep. But something woke him; he lay and listened, hearing nothing. He remembered suddenly and vividly the night she had balanced between life and death, and he had awakened to the echo of a sob which was not repeated; in sudden fright he jumped up and went to her, bent down and touched her head. She was lying face down. "You cry?" he whispered, and she shook her head rapidly. He grunted and went back to bed.

It was the ninth week and it was raining; he plodded homeward through the black, shining streets, and when he turned into his own block and saw the dead, slick river stretching between him and the streetlight in front of his house, he experienced a moment of fantasy, of dreamlike disorientation; it seemed to him for a second that none of this had happened, that in a moment the car would flash by him and dip toward the curb momentarily while a limp body tumbled out, and he must run to it and take it indoors, and it would bleed, it would bleed, it might die. . . . He shook himself like a big dog and put his head down against the rain, saying *Stupid!* to his inner self. Nothing could be wrong, now. He had found a way to live, and live that way he would, and he would abide no change in it.

But there was a change, and he knew it before he entered the house; his window, facing the street, had a dull orange glow which could not have been given it by the street light alone. But maybe she was reading one of those paperback novels he had inherited with the apartment; maybe she had to use the bedpan or was just looking at the clock . . . but the thoughts did not comfort him; he was sick with an unaccountable fear as he unlocked the hall door. His own entrance showed light through the crack at the bottom; he dropped his keys as he fumbled with them, and at last opened the door.

He gasped as if he had been struck in the solar plexus. The bed was made, flat, neat, and she was not in it. He spun around; his frantic gaze saw her and passed her before he could believe his eyes. Tall, queenly in her red housecoat, she stood at the other end of the room, by the sink.

He stared at her in amazement. She came to him, and as he filled his lungs for one of his grating yells, she put a finger on her lips and, lightly, her other hand across his mouth. Neither of these gestures, both even, would have been enough to quiet him ordinarily, but there was something else about her, something which did not wait for what he might do and would not quail before him if he did it. He was instantly confused, and silent. He stared after her as, without breaking stride, she passed him and gently closed the door. She took his hand, but the keys were in the way; she drew them from his fingers and tossed them on the table and then took his hand again, firmly. She was sure, decisive; she was one who had thought things out and weighed and discarded, and now knew what to do. But she was triumphant in some way, too; she had the poise of a victor and the radiance of the witness to a miracle. He could cope with her helplessness, of any kind, to any degree, but this—he had to think, and she gave him no time to think.

She led him to the bed and put her hands on his shoulders, turning him and making him sit down. She sat close to him, her face alight, and when again he filled his lungs, "Shh!" she hissed, sharply, and smilingly covered his mouth with her hand. She took his shoulders again and looked straight into his eyes, and said clearly, "I can talk now, I can talk!"

Numbly he gaped at her.

"Three days already, it was a secret, it was a surprise." Her voice was husky, hoarse even, but very clear and deeper than her slight body indicated. "I been practicing, to be sure. I'm all right again, I'm all right. You fix everything!" she said, and laughed.

Hearing that laugh, seeing the pride and joy in her face, he could take nothing away from her. "Ahh . . ." he said, wonderingly.

She laughed again. "I can go, I can go!" she sang. She leapt up suddenly and pirouetted, and leaned over him laughing. He gazed up at her and her flying hair, and squinted his eyes as he would looking into the sun. "Go?" he blared, the pressure of his confusion forcing the syllable out as an explosive shout.

She sobered immediately, and sat down again close to him. "Oh, honey, don't, *don't* look as if you was knifed or something. You know I can't camp on you, live off you, just for*ever!*"

"No, no you stay," he blurted, anguish in his face.

"Now look," she said, speaking simply and slowly as to a child. "I'm all well again, I can talk now. It wouldn't be right, me staying, locked up here, that bedpan and all. Now wait, wait," she said quickly before he could form a word, "I don't mean I'm not grateful, you been . . . you been, well, I just can't tell you. Look, nobody in my life ever did anything like this, I mean, I had to run away when I was thirteen, I done all sorts of bad things. And I got treated . . . I mean, nobody else . . . look, here's what I mean, up to now I'd steal, I'd rob anybody, what the hell. What I mean, why not, you see?" She shook him gently to make him see; then, recognizing the blankness and misery of his expression, she wet her lips and started over. "What I'm trying to say is, you been so kind, all this—" She waved her hand at the blue rabbit, the turtle tank, everything in the room— "I can't take any more. I mean, not a thing, not breakfast. If I could pay you back some way, no matter what, I would, you know I would." There was a tinge of bitterness in her husky voice. "Nobody can pay you anything. You don't need anything or anybody. I can't give you anything you need, or do anything for you that needs doing, you do it all yourself. If there was something you wanted from me—" She curled her hands inward and placed her fingertips between her breasts, inclining her head with a strange submissiveness that made him ache. "But no, you fix everything," she mimicked. There was no mockery in it.

"No, no, you don't go," he whispered harshly.

She patted his cheek, and her eyes loved him. "I do go," she said, smiling. Then the smile disappeared. "I got to explain to you, those hoods who cut me, I asked for that. I goofed. I was doing something real bad— well, I'll tell you. I was a runner, know what I mean? I mean dope, I was selling it."

He looked at her blankly. He was not catching one

word in ten; he was biting and biting only on emptiness and uselessness, aloneness, and the terrible truth of this room without her or the blue rabbit or anything else but what it had contained all these years—linoleum with the design scrubbed off, six novels he couldn't read, a stove waiting for someone to cook for, grime and regularity and who needs you?

She misunderstood his expression. "Honey, honey, don't look at me like that, I'll never do it again. I only did it because I didn't care, I used to get glad when people hurt themselves; yeah, I mean that. I never knew someone could be kind, like you; I always thought that was sort of a lie, like the movies. Nice but not real, not for me.

"But I have to tell you, I swiped a cache, my God, twenty, twenty-two G's worth. I had it all of forty minutes, they caught up with me." Her eyes widened and saw things not in the room. "With a razor, he went to hit me with it so hard he broke it on top of the car door. He hit me here *down* and here *up,* I guess he was going to gut me but the razor was busted." She expelled air from her nostrils, and her gaze came back into the room. "I guess I got the lump on the head when they threw me out of the car. I guess that's why I couldn't talk, I heard of that. Oh *honey!* Don't look like that, you're tearing me apart!"

He looked at her dolefully and wagged his big head helplessly from side to side. She knelt before him suddenly and took both his hands. "Listen, you *got* to understand. I was going to slide out while you were working but I stayed just so I could make you understand. After all you done. . . . See, I'm well, I can't stay cooped up in one room forever. If I could, I'd get work some place near here and see you all the time, honest I would. But my life isn't worth a rubber dime in this town. I got to leave here and that means I got to leave town. I'll be all right, honey. I'll write to you; I'll never forget you, how could I?"

She was far ahead of him. He had grasped that she wanted to leave him; the next thing he understood was that she wanted to leave town too.

"You don't go," he choked. "You need me."

"You don't need me," she said fondly, "and I don't need you. It comes to that, honey; it's the way you fixed it. It's the right way; can't you see that?"

Right in there was the third thing he understood.

He stood up slowly, feeling her hands slide from his, from his knees to the floor as he stepped away from her. "Oh God!" she cried from the floor where she knelt, "you're killing me, taking it this way! Can't you be happy for me?"

He stumbled across the room and caught himself on the lower shelf of the china closet. He looked back and forward along the dark, echoing corridor of his years, stretching so far and drearily, and he looked at this short bright segment slipping away from him. . . . He heard her quick footsteps behind him and when he turned he had the flatiron in his hand. She never saw it. She came to him bright-faced, pleading, and he put out his arms and she ran inside, and the iron curved around and crashed into the back of her head.

He lowered her gently down on the linoleum and stood for a long time over her, crying quietly.

Then he put the iron away and filled the kettle and a saucepan with water, and in the saucepan he put needles and a clamp and thread and little slabs of sponge and a knife and pliers. From the gateleg table and from a drawer he got his two plastic tablecloths and began arranging them on the bed.

"I fix everything," he murmured as he worked, "Fix it right."

MICROCOSMIC GOD

HERE IS a story about a man who had too much power, and a man who took too much, but don't worry; I'm not going political on you. The man who had the power was named James Kidder and the other was his banker.

Kidder was quite a guy. He was a scientist and he lived on a small island off the New England coast all by himself. He wasn't the dwarfed little gnome of a mad scientist you read about. His hobby wasn't personal profit, and he wasn't a megalomaniac with a Russian name and no scruples. He wasn't insidious, and he wasn't even particularly subversive. He kept his hair cut and his nails clean and lived and thought like a reasonable human being. He was slightly on the baby-faced side; he was inclined to be a hermit; he was short and plump and—brilliant. His specialty was biochemistry, and he was always called *Mr.* Kidder. Not "Dr." Not "Professor." Just Mr. Kidder.

He was an odd sort of apple and always had been. He had never graduated from any college or university because he found them too slow for him, and too rigid in their approach to education. He couldn't get used to the idea that perhaps his professors knew what they were talking about. That went for his texts, too. He was always asking questions, and didn't mind very much when they were embarrassing. He considered Gregor Mendel a bungling liar, Darwin an amusing philosopher, and Luther Burbank a sensationalist. He never opened his mouth without leaving his victim feeling breathless. If he was talking to someone who had knowledge, he went in there and got it, leaving his victim breathless. If he was talking to someone whose knowledge was already in his possession, he only asked repeatedly, "How do you know?" His most delectable pleasure was cutting a fanatical eugenicist into conversational ribbons. So people left him alone and never, never asked him to tea. He was polite, but not politic.

He had a little money of his own, and with it he leased the island and built himself a laboratory. Now I've mentioned that he was a biochemist. But being what he was, he couldn't keep his nose in his own field. It wasn't too remarkable when he made an intellectual excursion wide enough to perfect a method of crystallizing Vitamin B1 profitably by the ton—if anyone wanted it by the ton. He got a lot of money for it. He bought his island outright and put eight hundred men to work on an acre and a half of his ground, adding to his laboratory and building equipment. He got to messing around with sisal fiber, found out how to fuse it, and boomed the banana industry by producing a practically unbreakable cord from the stuff.

You remember the popularizing demonstration he put on at Niagara, don't you? That business of running a line of the new cord from bank to bank over the rapids and suspending a ten-ton truck from the middle of it by razor edges resting on the cord? That's why ships now moor themselves with what looks like heaving line, no thicker than a lead pencil, that can be coiled on reels like garden hose. Kidder made cigarette money out of that, too. He went out and bought himself a cyclotron with part of it.

After that money wasn't money any more. It was large numbers in little books. Kidder used little amounts of it to have food and equipment sent out to him, but after a while that stopped, too. His bank dispatched a messenger by sea-plane to find out if Kidder was still alive. The man returned two days later in a bemused state, having been amazed something awesome at the things he'd seen out there. Kidder was alive, all right, and he was turning out a surplus of good food in an astonishingly simplified synthetic form. The bank wrote immediately and wanted to know if Mr. Kidder, in his own interest, was willing to release the secret of his dirtless farming. Kidder replied that he would be glad to, and inclosed the formulas. In a P. S. he said that he hadn't sent the information ashore because he hadn't realized anyone would be interested. That from a man who was responsible for the greatest sociological change in the second half of the twentieth century—factory farming. It made him richer; I mean it made his bank richer. He didn't give a rap.

But Kidder didn't really get started until about eight months after the messenger's visit. For a biochemist who couldn't even be called "Doctor" he did pretty well. Here is a partial list of the things that he turned out:

A commercially feasible plan for making an aluminum alloy stronger than the best steel so that it could be used as a structural metal.

An exhibition gadget he called a light pump, which worked on the theory that light is a form of matter and therefore subject to physical and electromagnetic laws. Seal a room with a single light source, beam a cylindrical vibratory magnetic field to it from the pump, and the light will be led down it. Now pass the light through Kidder's "lens"—a ring which perpetuates an electric field along the lines of a high-speed iris-type camera shutter. Below this is the heart of the light pump—a ninety-eight-per-cent efficient light absorber, crystalline, which, in a sense, *loses* the light in its internal facets. The effect of darkening the room with this apparatus is slight but measurable. Pardon my layman's language, but that's the general idea.

Synthetic chlorophyll—by the barrel.

An airplane propeller efficient at eight times sonic speed.

A cheap goo you brush on over old paint, let harden, and then peel off like strips of cloth. The old paint comes with it. That one made friends fast.

A self-sustaining atomic disintegration of uranium's isotope 238, which is two hundred times as plentiful as the old stand-by, U-235.

That will do for the present. If I may repeat myself;

for a biochemist who couldn't even be called "Doctor," he did pretty well.

Kidder was apparently unconscious of the fact that he held power enough on his little island to become master of the world. His mind simply didn't run to things like that. As long as he was left alone with his experiments, he was well content to leave the rest of the world to its own clumsy and primitive devices. He couldn't be reached except by a radiophone of his own design, and its only counterpart was locked in a vault of his Boston bank. Only one man could operate it. The extraordinarily sensitive transmitter would respond only to Conant's own body vibrations. Kidder had instructed Conant that he was not to be disturbed except by messages of the greatest moment. His ideas and patents, what Conant could pry out of him, were released under pseudonyms known only to Conant—Kidder didn't care.

The result, of course, was an infiltration of the most astonishing advancements since the dawn of civilization. The nation profited—the world profited. But most of all, the bank profited. It began to get a little oversize. It began getting its fingers into other pies. It grew more fingers and had to bake more figurative pies. Before many years had passed, it was so big that, using Kidder's many weapons, it almost matched Kidder in power.

Almost.

Now stand by while I squelch those fellows in the lower left-hand corner who've been saying all this while that Kidder's slightly improbable; that no man could ever perfect himself in so many ways in so many sciences.

Well, you're right. Kidder was a genius—granted. But his genius was not creative. He was, to the core, a student. He applied what he knew, what he saw, and what he was taught. When first he began working in his new laboratory on his island he reasoned something like this:

"Everything I know is what I have been taught by the sayings and writings of people who have studied the sayings and writings of people who have—and so on. Once in a while someone stumbles on something new and he or someone cleverer uses the idea and disseminates it. But for each one that finds something really new, a couple of million gather and pass on information that is already current. I'd know more if I could get the jump on evolutionary trends. It takes too long to wait for the accidents that increase man's knowledge—my knowledge. If I had ambition enough now to figure out how to travel ahead in time, I could skim the surface of the future and just dip down when I saw something interesting. But time isn't that way. It can't be left behind or tossed ahead. What else is left?

"Well, there's the proposition of speeding intellectual evolution so that I can observe what it cooks up. That seems a bit inefficient. It would involve more labor to discipline human minds to that extent than it would to simply apply myself along those lines. But I can't apply myself that way. No one man can.

"I'm licked. I can't speed myself up, and I can't speed other men's minds up. Isn't there an alternative? There must be—somewhere, somehow, there's got to be an answer."

So it was on this, and not on eugenics, or light pumps, or botany, or atomic physics, that James Kidder applied himself. For a practical man he found the problem slightly on the metaphysical side; but he attacked it with typical thoroughness, using his own peculiar brand of logic. Day after day he wandered over the island, throwing shells impotently at sea gulls and swearing richly. Then came a time when he sat indoors and brooded. And only then did he get feverishly to work.

He worked in his own field, biochemistry, and concentrated mainly on two things—genetics and animal metabolism. He learned, and filed away in his insatiable mind, many things having nothing to do with the problem in hand, and very little of what he wanted. But he piled that little on what little he knew or guessed, and in time had quite a collection of known factors to work with. His approach was characteristically unorthodox. He did things on the order of multiplying apples by pears, and balancing equations by adding log $\sqrt{-1}$ to one side and ^{00} to the other. He made mistakes, but only one of a kind, and later, only one of a species. He spent so many hours at his microscope that he had quit work for two days to get rid of a hallucination that his heart was pumping his own blood through the mike. He did nothing by trial and error because he disapproved of the method as sloppy.

And he got results. He was lucky to begin with and even luckier when he formularized the law of probability and reduced it to such low terms that he knew almost to the item what experiments not to try. When the cloudy, viscous semifluid on the watch glass began to move itself he knew he was on the right track. When it began to seek food on its own he began to be excited. When it divided and, in a few hours, redivided, and each part grew and divided again, he was triumphant, for he had created life.

He nursed his brain children and sweated and strained over them, and he designed baths of various vibrations for them, and inoculated and dosed and sprayed them. Each move he made taught him the next. And out of his tanks and tubes and incubators came amoebalike creatures, and then ciliated animalcules, and more and more rapidly he produced animals with eye spots, nerve cysts, and then—victory of victories—a real blastopod, possessed of many cells instead of one. More slowly he developed a gastropod, but once he had it, it was not too difficult for him to give it organs, each with a specified function, each inheritable.

Then came cultured mollusklike things, and creatures with more and more perfected gills. The day that a nondescript thing wriggled up an inclined board out of a tank, threw flaps over its gills and feebly breathed air, Kidder quit work and went to the other end of the island and got disgustingly drunk. Hangover and all, he was soon back in the lab, forgetting to eat, forgetting to sleep, tearing into his problem.

He turned into a scientific byway and ran down his other great triumph—accelerated metabolism. He extracted and refined the stimulating factors in alcohol, coca, heroin, and Mother Nature's prize dope runner, *cannabis indica*. Like the scientist who, in analyzing the various clotting agents for blood treatments, found that oxalic acid and oxalic acid alone was the active factor, Kidder isolated the accelerators and decelerators, the stimulants and soporifics, in every substance that ever - undermined a man's morality and/or caused a "noble experiment." In the process he found one thing he needed badly—a colorless elixir that made sleep the unnecessary and avoidable waster of time it should be. Then and there he went on a twenty-four-hour shift.

He artificially synthesized the substances he had isolated, and in doing so sloughed away a great many useless components. He pursued the subject along the lines of radiations and vibrations. He discovered something in the longer reds which, when projected through a vessel full of air vibrating in the supersonics, and then polarized, speeded up the heartbeat of small animals twenty to one. They ate twenty times as much, grew twenty times as fast, and—died twenty times sooner than they should have.

Kidder built a huge hermetically sealed room. Above it was another room, the same length and breadth but not quite as high. This was his control chamber. The large room was divided into four sealed sections, each with its individual miniature cranes and derricks—handling machinery of all kinds. There were also trapdoors fitted with air locks leading from the upper to the lower room.

By this time the other laboratory had produced a warm-blooded, snake-skinned quadruped with an astonishingly rapid life cycle—a generation every eight days, a life span of about fifteen. Like the echidna, it was oviparous and mammalian. Its period of gestation was six hours; the eggs hatched in three; the young reached sexual maturity in another four days. Each female laid four eggs and lived just long enough to care for the young after they hatched. The male generally died two or three hours after mating. The creatures were highly adaptable. They were small—not more than three inches long, two inches to the shoulder from the ground. Their forepaws had three digits and a triple-jointed, opposed thumb. They were attuned to life in an atmosphere with a large ammonia content. Kidder bred four of the creatures and put one group in each section of the sealed room.

Then he was ready. With his controlled atmospheres he varied temperatures, oxygen content, humidity. He killed them off like flies with excesses of, for instance, carbon dioxide, and the survivors bred their physical resistance into the next generation. Periodically he would switch the eggs from one sealed section to another to keep the strains varied. And rapidly, under these controlled conditions, the creatures began to evolve.

This, then, was the answer to his problem. He couldn't speed up mankind's intellectual advancement enough to have it teach him the things his incredible mind yearned for. He couldn't speed himself up. So he created a new race—a race which would develop and evolve so fast that it would surpass the civilization of man; and from them he would learn.

They were completely in Kidder's power. Earth's normal atmosphere would poison them, as he took care to demonstrate to every fourth generation. They would make no attempt to escape from him. They would live their lives and progress and make their little trial-and-error experiments hundreds of times faster than man did. They had the edge on man, for they had Kidder to guide them. It took man six thousand years really to discover science, three hundred to put it to work. It took Kidder's creatures two hundred days to equal man's mental attainments. And from then on— Kidder's spasmodic output made the late, great Tom Edison look like a home handicrafter.

He called them Neoterics, and he teased them into working for him. Kidder was inventive in an ideological way; that is, he could dream up impossible propositions providing he didn't have to work them out. For example, he wanted the Neoterics to figure out for themselves how to build shelters out of porous material. He created the need for such shelters by subjecting one of the sections to a high-pressure rainstorm which flattened the inhabitants. The Neoterics promptly devised waterproof shelters out of the thin waterproof material he piled in one corner. Kidder immediately blew down the flimsy structure with a blast of cold air. They built them up again so that they resisted both wind and rain. Kidder lowered the temperature so abruptly that they could not adjust their bodies to it. They heated their shelters with tiny braziers. Kidder promptly turned up the heat until they began to roast to death. After a few deaths, one of their bright boys figured out how to build a strong insulant house by using three-ply rubberoid, with the middle layer perforated thousands of times to create tiny air pockets.

Using such tactics, Kidder forced them to develop a highly advanced little culture. He caused a drought in one section and a liquid surplus in another, and then opened the partition between them. Quite a spectacular war was fought, and Kidder's notebooks filled with information about military tactics and weapons. Then there was the vaccine they developed against the common cold—the reason why that affliction has been absolutely stamped out in the world today, for it was one of the things that Conant, the bank president, got hold of. He spoke to Kidder over the radiophone one winter afternoon with a voice so hoarse from laryngitis that Kidder sent him a vial of vaccine and told him briskly not to ever call him again in such a disgustingly inaudible state. Conant had it analyzed and again Kidder's accounts and the bank's swelled.

At first, Kidder merely supplied the materials he thought they might need, but when they developed an intelligence equal to the task of fabricating their own from the elements at hand, he gave each section a stock of raw materials. The process for really strong aluminum was developed when he built in a huge plunger in one of the sections, which reached from wall to wall and was designed to descend at the rate of four inches a day until it crushed whatever was at the bottom. The Neoterics, in self-defense, used what strong material they had in hand to stop the inexorable

death that threatened them. But Kidder had seen to it
that they had nothing but aluminum oxide and a scat-
tering of other elements, plus plenty of electric power.
At first they ran up dozens of aluminum pillars; when
these were crushed and twisted they tried shaping them
so that the soft metal would take more weight. When
that failed they quickly built stronger ones; and when
the plunger was halted, Kidder removed one of the
pillars and analyzed it. It was hardened aluminum,
stronger and tougher than molybd steel.

Experience taught Kidder that he had to make certain changes to increase his power over his Neoterics
before they got too ingenious. There were things that
could be done with atomic power that he was curious
about; but he was not willing to trust his little super-
scientists with a thing like that unless they could be
trusted to use it strictly according to Hoyle. So he in-
stituted a rule of fear. The most trivial departure from
what he chose to consider the right way of doing things
resulted in instant death of half a tribe. If he was trying to develop a Diesel-type power plant, for instance,
that would operate without a flywheel, and a bright
young Neoteric used any of the materials for archi-
tectural purposes, half the tribe immediately died. Of
course, they had developed a written language; it was
Kidder's own. The teletype in a glass-enclosed area
in a corner of each section was a shrine. Any directions that were given on it were obeyed, or else. . . .
After this innovation, Kidder's work was much sim-
pler. There was no need for any indirection. Anything
he wanted done was done. No matter how impossible
his commands, three or four generations of Neoterics
could find a way to carry them out.

This quotation is from a paper that one of Kidder's
high-speed telescopic cameras discovered being cir-
culated among the younger Neoterics. It is translated
from the highly simplified script of the Neoterics.

"These edicts shall be followed by each Neoteric
upon pain of death, which punishment will be inflicted
by the tribe upon the individual to protect the tribe
against him.

"Priority of interest and tribal and individual effort

is to be given the commands that appear on the word machine.

"Any misdirection of material or power, or use thereof for any other purpose than the carrying out of the machine's commands, unless no command appears, shall be punishable by death.

"Any information regarding the problem at hand, or ideas or experiments which might conceivably bear upon it, are to become the property of the tribe.

"Any individual failing to cooperate in the tribal effort, or who can be termed guilty of not expending his full efforts in the work; or the suspicion thereof shall be subject to the death penalty."

Such are the results of complete domination. This paper impressed Kidder as much as it did because it was completely spontaneous. It was the Neoterics' own creed, developed by them for their own greatest good.

And so at last Kidder had his fulfillment. Crouched in the upper room, going from telescope to telescope, running off slowed-down films from his high-speed cameras, he found himself possessed of a tractable, dynamic source of information. Housed in the great square building with its four half-acre sections was a new world, to which he was god.

Conant's mind was similar to Kidder's in that its approach to any problem was along the shortest distance between any two points, regardless of whether that approach was along the line of most or least resistance. His rise to the bank presidency was a history of ruthless moves whose only justification was that they got him what he wanted. Like an over-efficient general, he would never vanquish an enemy through sheer force of numbers alone. He would also skillfully flank his enemy, not on one side, but on both. Innocent bystanders were creatures deserving no consideration.

The time he took over a certain thousand-acre property, for instance, from a man named Grady, he was not satisfied with only the title to the land. Grady was an airport owner—had been all his life, and his father before him. Conant exerted every kind of pressure on the man and found him unshakable. Finally judicious persuasion led the city officials to dig a sewer right across the middle of the field, quite efficiently wrecking Grady's business. Knowing that this would supply Grady, who was a wealthy man, with motive for revenge, Conant took over Grady's bank at half again its value and caused it to fold up. Grady lost every cent he had and ended his life in an asylum. Conant was very proud of his tactics.

Like many another who has had Mammon by the tail, Conant did not know when to let go. His vast organization yielded him more money and power than any other concern in history, and yet he was not satisfied. Conant and money were like Kidder and knowledge. Conant's pyramided enterprises were to him what the Neoterics were to Kidder. Each had made his private world; each used it for his instruction and profit. Kidder, though, disturbed nobody but his Neoterics. Even so, Conant was not wholly villainous. He was a shrewd man, and had discovered early the value of pleasing people. No man can rob successfully over a period of years without pleasing the people he robs. The technique for doing this is highly involved, but master it and you can start your own mint.

Conant's one great fear was that Kidder would some day take an interest in world events and begin to become opinionated. Good heavens—the potential power he had! A little matter like swinging an election could be managed by a man like Kidder as easily as turning over in bed. The only thing he could do was to call him periodically and see if there was anything that Kidder needed to keep himself busy. Kidder appreciated this. Conant, once in a while, would suggest something to Kidder that intrigued him, something that would keep him deep in his hermitage for a few weeks. The light pump was one of the results of Conant's imagination. Conant bet him it couldn't be done. Kidder did it.

One afternoon Kidder answered the squeal of the radiophone's signal. Swearing mildly, he shut off the film he was watching and crossed the compound to the old laboratory. He went to the radiophone, threw a switch. The squealing stopped.

"Well?"

"Hello," said Conant. "Busy?"

"Not very," said Kidder. He was delighted with the pictures his camera had caught, showing the skillful work of a gang of Neoterics synthesizing rubber out of pure sulphur. He would rather have liked to tell Conant about it, but somehow he had never got around to telling Conant about the Neoterics, and he didn't see why he should start now.

Conant said, "Er . . . Kidder, I was down at the club the other day and a bunch of us were filling up an evening with loose talk. Something came up which might interest you."

"What?"

"Couple of the utilities boys there. You know the power setup in this country, don't you? Thirty per cent atomic, the rest hydroelectric, Diesel and steam?"

"I hadn't known," said Kidder, who was as innocent as a babe of current events.

"Well, we were arguing about what chance a new power source would have. One of the men there said it would be smarter to produce a new power and then talk about it. Another one waived that; said he couldn't name that new power, but he could describe it. Said it would have to have everything that present power sources have, plus one or two more things. It could be cheaper, for instance. It could be more efficient. It might supersede the others by being easier to carry from the power plant to the consumer. See what I mean? Any one of these factors might prove a new source of power competitive to the others. What I'd like to see is a new power with *all* of these factors. What do you think of it?"

"Not impossible."

"Think not?"

"I'll try it."

"Keep me posted." Conant's transmitter clicked off. The switch was a little piece of false front that Kidder had built into the set, which was something that Conant didn't know. The set switched itself off when

Conant moved from it. After the switch's sharp crack, Kidder heard the banker mutter, "If he does it, I'm all set. If he doesn't, at least the crazy fool will keep himself busy on the isl—"

Kidder eyed the radiophone for an instant with raised eyebrows, and then shrugged them down again with his shoulders. It was quite evident that Conant had something up his sleeve, but Kidder wasn't worried. Who on earth would want to disturb him? He wasn't bothering anybody. He went back to the Neoterics' building, full of the new power idea.

Eleven days later Kidder called Conant and gave specific instructions on how to equip his receiver with a facsimile set which would enable Kidder to send written matter over the air. As soon as this was done and Kidder informed, the biochemist for once in his life spoke at some length.

"Conant—you implied that a new power source that would be cheaper, more efficient and more easily transmitted than any now in use did not exist. You might be interested in the little generator I have just set up.

"It has power, Conant—unbelievable power. Broadcast. A beautiful little tight beam. Here—catch this on the facsimile recorder." Kidder slipped a sheet of paper under the clips of his transmitter and it appeared on Conant's set. "Here's the wiring diagram for a power receiver. Now listen. The beam is so tight, so highly directional, that not three-thousandths of one per cent of the power would be lost in a two-thousand-mile transmission. The power system is closed. That is, any drain on the beam returns a signal along it to the transmitter, which automatically steps up to increase the power output. It has a limit, but it's way up. And something else. This little gadget of mine can send out eight different beams with a total horsepower output of around eight thousand per minute per beam. From each beam you can draw enough power to turn the page of a book or fly a superstratosphere plane. Hold on—I haven't finished yet. Each beam, as I told you before, returns a signal from receiver to transmitter. This not only controls the power output of the beam, but directs it. Once contact is made, the beam will never let go. It will follow the receiver anywhere. You can power land, air or water vehicles with it, as well as any stationary plant. Like it?"

Conant, who was a banker and not a scientist, wiped his shining pate with the back of his hand and said, "I've never known you to steer me wrong yet, Kidder. How about the cost of this thing?"

"High," said Kidder promptly. "As high as an atomic plant. But there are no high-tension lines, no wires, no pipelines, no nothing. The receivers are little more complicated than a radio set. Transmitter is—well, that's quite a job."

"Didn't take you long," said Conant.

"No," said Kidder, "it didn't, did it?" It was the life-work of nearly twelve hundred highly cultured people, but Kidder wasn't going into that. "Of course, the one I have here's just a model."

Conant's voice was strained. "A—model? And it de-livers—"

"Over sixty-thousand horsepower," said Kidder gleefully.

"Good heavens! In a full-sized machine—why, one transmitter would be enough to—" The possibilities of the thing choked Conant for a moment. "How is it fueled?"

"It isn't," said Kidder. "I won't begin to explain it. I've tapped a source of power of unimaginable force. It's—well, big. So big that it can't be misused."

"What?" snapped Conant. "What do you mean by that?"

Kidder cocked an eyebrow. Conant *had* something up his sleeve, then. At this second indication of it, Kidder, the least suspicious of men, began to put himself on guard. "I mean just what I say," he said evenly. "Don't try too hard to understand me—I barely savvy it myself. But the source of this power is a monstrous resultant caused by the unbalance of two previously equalized forces. Those equalized forces are cosmic in quantity. Actually, the forces are those which make suns, crush atoms the way they crushed those that compose the companion of Sirius. It's not anything you can fool with."

"I don't—" said Conant, and his voice ended puzzledly.

"I'll give you a parallel of it," said Kidder. "Suppose you take two rods, one in each hand. Place their tips together and push. As long as your pressure is directly along their long axes, the pressure is equalized; right and left hands cancel each other. Now I come along; I put out one finger and touch the rods ever so lightly where they come together. They snap out of line violently; you break a couple of knuckles. The resultant force is at right angles to the original forces you exerted. My power transmitter is on the same principle. It takes an infinitesimal amount of energy to throw those forces out of line. Easy enough when you know how to do it. The important question is whether or not you can control the resultant when you get it. I can."

"I—see." Conant indulged in a four-second gloat. "Heaven help the utility companies. I don't intend to. Kidder—I want a full-size power transmitter."

Kidder clucked into the radiophone. "Ambitious, aren't you? I haven't a staff out here, Conant—you know that. And I can't be expected to build four or five thousand tons of apparatus myself."

"I'll have five hundred engineers and laborers out there in forty-eight hours."

"You will not. Why bother me with it? I'm quite happy here, Conant, and one of the reasons is that I've no one to get in my hair."

"Oh, now, Kidder—don't be like that—I'll pay you—"

"You haven't got that much money," said Kidder briskly. He flipped the switch on his set. *His* switch worked.

Conant was furious. He shouted into the phone several times, then began to lean on the signal button. On his island, Kidder let the thing squeal and went back to his projection room. He was sorry he had sent the diagram of the receiver to Conant. It would have been interesting to power a plane or a car with the model transmitter he had taken from the Neoterics. But if

Conant was going to be that way about it—well, anyway, the receiver would be no good without the transmitter. Any radio engineer would understand the diagram, but not the beam which activated it. And Conant wouldn't get his beam.

Pity he didn't know Conant well enough.

Kidder's days were endless sorties into learning. He never slept, nor did his Neoterics. He ate regularly every five hours, exercised for half an hour in every twelve. He did not keep track of time, for it meant nothing to him. Had he wanted to know the date, or the year, even, he knew he could get it from Conant. He didn't care, that's all. The time that was not spent in observation was used in developing new problems for the Neoterics. His thoughts just now ran to defense. The idea was born in his conversation with Conant; now the idea was primary, its motivation something of no importance. The Neoterics were working on a vibration field of quasi-electrical nature. Kidder could see little practical value in such a thing—an invisible wall which would kill any living thing which touched it. But still—the idea was intriguing.

He stretched and moved away from the telescope in the upper room through which he had been watching his creations at work. He was profoundly happy here in the large control room. Leaving it to go to the old laboratory for a bite to eat was a thing he hated to do. He felt like bidding it good-by each time he walked across the compound, and saying a glad hello when he returned. A little amused at himself, he went out.

There was a black blob—a distant power boat—a few miles off the island, toward the mainland. Kidder stopped and stared distastefully at it. A white petal of spray was affixed to each side of the black body—it was coming toward him. He snorted, thinking of the time a yachtload of silly fools had landed out of curiosity one afternoon, spewed themselves over his beloved island, peppered him with lame-brained questions, and thrown his nervous equilibrium out for days. Lord, how he hated *people!*

The thought of unpleasantness bred two more

thoughts that played half-consciously with his mind as he crossed the compound and entered the old laboratory. One was that perhaps it might be wise to surround his buildings with a field of force of some kind and post warnings for trespassers. The other thought was of Conant and the vague uneasiness the man had been sending to him through the radiophone these last weeks. His suggestion, two days ago, that a power plant be built on the island—horrible idea!

Conant rose from a laboratory bench as Kidder walked in.

They looked at each other wordlessly for a long moment. Kidder hadn't seen the bank president in years. The man's presence, he found, made his scalp crawl.

"Hello," said Conant genially. "You're looking fit."

Kidder grunted. Conant eased his unwieldy body back onto the bench and said, "Just to save you the energy of asking questions, Mr. Kidder, I arrived two hours ago on a small boat. Rotten way to travel. I wanted to be a surprise to you; my two men rowed me the last couple of miles. You're not very well equipped here for defense, are you? Why, anyone could slip up on you the way I did."

"Who'd want to?" growled Kidder. The man's voice edged annoyingly into his brain. He spoke too loudly for such a small room; at least, Kidder's hermit's ears felt that way. Kidder shrugged and went about preparing a light meal for himself.

"Well," drawled the banker. "I might want to." He drew out a Dow-metal cigar case. "Mind if I smoke?"

"I do," said Kidder sharply.

Conant laughed easily and put the cigars away. "I might," he said, "want to urge you to let me build that power station on this island."

"Radiophone work?"

"Oh, yes. But now that I'm here you can't switch me off. Now—how about it?"

"I haven't changed my mind."

"Oh, but you should, Kidder, you should. Think of it—think of the good it would do for the masses of people that are now paying exorbitant power bills!"

"I hate the masses! Why do you have to build here?"

"Oh, that. It's an ideal location. You own the island; work could begin here without causing any comment whatsoever. The plant would spring full-fledged on the power markets of the country, having been built in secret. The island can be made impregnable."

"I don't want to be bothered."

"We wouldn't bother you. We'd build on the north end of the island—a mile and a quarter from you and your work. Ah—by the way—where's the model of the power transmitter?"

Kidder, with his mouth full of synthesized food, waved a hand at a small table on which stood the model, a four-foot, amazingly intricate device of plastic and steel and tiny coils.

Conant rose and went over to look at it. "Actually works, eh?" He sighed deeply and said, "Kidder, I really hate to do this, but I want to build that plant rather badly. Carson! Robbins!"

Two bull-necked individuals stepped out from their hiding places in the corners of the room. One idly dangled a revolver by its trigger guard. Kidder looked blankly from one to the other of them.

"These gentlemen will follow my orders implicitly, Kidder. In half an hour a party will land here—engineers, contractors. They will start surveying the north end of the island for the construction of the power plant. These boys here feel about the same way I do as far as you are concerned. Do we proceed with your cooperation or without it? It's immaterial to me whether or not you are left alive to continue your work. My engineers can duplicate your model."

Kidder said nothing. He had stopped chewing when he saw the gunmen, and only now remembered to swallow. He sat crouched over his plate without moving or speaking.

Conant broke the silence by walking to the door. "Robbins—can you carry that model there?" The big man put his gun away, lifted the model gently, and nodded. "Take it down to the beach and meet the other boat. Tell Mr. Johansen, the engineer, that this is the model he is to work from." Robbins went out. Conant turned to Kidder. "There's no need for us to anger our-selves," he said oilily. "I think you are stubborn, but I don't hold it against you. I know how you feel. You'll be left alone; you have my promise. But I mean to go ahead on this job, and a small thing like your life can't stand in my way."

Kidder said, "Get out of here." There were two swollen veins throbbing at his temples. His voice was low, and it shook.

"Very well. Good day, Mr. Kidder. Oh—by the way —you're a clever devil." No one had ever referred to the scholastic Mr. Kidder that way before. "I realize the possibility of your blasting us off the island. I wouldn't do it if I were you. I'm willing to give you what you want—privacy. I want the same thing in re-turn. If anything happens to me while I'm here, the island will be bombed by someone who is working for me. I'll admit they might fail. If they do, the United States government will take a hand. You wouldn't want that, would you? That's rather a big thing for one man to fight. The same thing goes if the plant is sab-otaged in any way after I go back to the mainland. You might be killed. You will most certainly be bothered interminably. Thanks for your . . . er . . . cooperation." The banker smirked and walked out, followed by his taciturn gorilla.

Kidder sat there for a long time without moving. Then he shook his head, rested it in his palms. He was badly frightened; not so much because his life was in danger, but because his privacy and his work—his world—were threatened. He was hurt and bewildered. He wasn't a businessman. He couldn't handle men. All his life he had run away from human beings and what they represented to him. He was like a frightened child when men closed in on him.

Cooling a little, he wondered vaguely what would happen when the power plant opened. Certainly the government would be interested. Unless—unless by then Conant was the government. That plant was an unimaginable source of power, and not only the kind of power that turned wheels. He rose and went back to the world that was home to him, a world where his motives were understood, and where there were those who could help him. Back at the Neoterics' building, he escaped yet again from the world of men into his work.

Kidder called Conant the following week, much to the banker's surprise. His two days on the island had got the work well under way, and he had left with the arrival of a shipload of laborers and material. He kept in close touch by radio with Johansen, the engineer in charge. It had been a blind job for Johansen and all the rest of the crew on the island. Only the bank's infinite resources could have hired such a man, or the picked gang with him.

Johansen's first reaction when he saw the model had been ecstatic. He wanted to tell his friends about this marvel; but the only radio set available was beamed to Conant's private office in the bank, and Conant's armed guards, one to every two workers, had strict orders to destroy any other radio transmitter on sight. About that time he realized that he was a prisoner on the island. His instant anger subsided when he reflected that being a prisoner at fifty thousand dollars a week wasn't too bad. Two of the laborers and an engineer thought differently, and got disgruntled a couple of days after they arrived. They disappeared one night—the same night that five shots were fired down on the beach. No questions were asked, and there was no more trouble.

Conant covered his surprise at Kidder's call and was as offensively jovial as ever. "Well, now! Anything I can do for you?"

"Yes," said Kidder. His voice was low, completely without expression. "I want you to issue a warning to your men not to pass the white line I have drawn five hundred yards north of my buildings, right across the island."

"Warning? Why, my dear fellow, they have orders that you are not to be disturbed on any account."

"You've ordered them. All right. Now warn them. I have an electric field surrounding my laboratories that will kill anything living which penetrates it. I don't want to have murder on my conscience. There will be no deaths unless there are trespassers. You'll inform your workers?"

"Oh, now Kidder," the banker expostulated. "That was totally unnecessary. You won't be bothered. Why —" But he found he was talking into a dead mike. He knew better than to call back. He called Johansen instead and told him about it. Johansen didn't like the sound of it, but he repeated the message and signed off. Conant liked that man. He was, for a moment, a little sorry that Johansen would never reach the mainland alive.

But that Kidder—he was beginning to be a problem. As long as his weapons were strictly defensive he was no real menace. But he would have to be taken care of when the plant was operating. Conant couldn't afford to have genius around him unless it was unquestionably on his side. The power transmitter and Conant's highly ambitious plans would be safe as long as Kidder was left to himself. Kidder knew that he could, for the time being, expect more sympathetic treatment from Conant than he could from a horde of government investigators.

Kidder only left his own enclosure once after the work began on the north end of the island, and it took all of his unskilled diplomacy to do it. Knowing the source of the plant's power, knowing what could happen if it were misused, he asked Conant's permission to inspect the great transmitter when it was nearly finished. Insuring his own life by refusing to report back to Conant until he was safe within his own laboratory again, he turned off his shield and walked up to the north end.

He saw an awe-inspiring sight. The four-foot model was duplicated nearly a hundred times as large. Inside a massive three-hundred-foot tower a space was packed nearly solid with the same bewildering maze of coils and bars that the Neoterics had built so delicately into their machine. At the top was a globe of polished golden alloy, the transmitting antenna. From it would stream thousands of tight beams of force, which could be tapped to any degree by corresponding thousands of receivers placed anywhere at any distance. Kidder learned that the receivers had already been built, but his informant, Johansen, knew little about that end of it and was saying less. Kidder checked over every detail of the structure, and when he was through he shook Johansen's hand admiringly.

"I didn't want this thing here," he said shyly, "and I don't. But I will say that it's a pleasure to see this kind of work."

"It's a pleasure to meet the man that invented it."

Kidder beamed. "I didn't invent it," he said. "Maybe some day I'll show you who did. I—well, good-by." He turned before he had a chance to say too much and marched off down the path.

"Shall I?" said a voice at Johansen's side. One of Conant's guards had his gun out.

Johansen knocked the man's arm down. "No." He scratched his head. "So that's the mysterious menace from the other end of the island. Eh! Why, he's a hell of a nice little feller!"

Built on the ruins of Denver, which was destroyed in the great Battle of the Rockies during the Western War, stands the most beautiful city in the world—our nation's capital. New Washington. In a circular room deep in the heart of the White House, the president, three army men and a civilian sat. Under the president's desk a dictaphone unostentatiously recorded every word that was said. Two thousand and more miles away, Conant hung over a radio receiver, tuned to receive the signals of the tiny transmitter in the civilian's side pocket.

One of the officers spoke.

"Mr. President, the 'impossible claims' made for this gentleman's product are absolutely true. He has proved beyond doubt each item on his prospectus."

The president glanced at the civilian, back at the officer. "I won't wait for your report," he said. "Tell me—what happened?"

Another of the army men mopped his face with a khaki bandanna. "I can't ask you to believe us, Mr.

President, but it's true all the same. Mr. Wright here has in his suitcase three or four dozen small . . . er . . . bombs—"

"They're not bombs," said Wright casually.

"All right. They're not bombs. Mr. Wright smashed two of them on an anvil with a sledge hammer. There was no result. He put two more in an electric furnace. They burned away like so much tin and cardboard. We dropped one down the barrel of a field piece and fired it. Still nothing." He paused and looked at the third officer, who picked up the account:

"We really got started then. We flew to the proving grounds, dropped one of the objects and flew to thirty thousand feet. From there, with a small hand detonator no bigger than your fist, Mr. Wright set the thing off. I've never seen anything like it. Forty acres of land came straight up at us, breaking up as it came. The concussion was terrific—you must have felt it here, four hundred miles away."

The president nodded. "I did. Seismographs on the other side of the Earth picked it up."

"The crater it left was a quarter of a mile deep at the center. Why, one plane load of those things could demolish any city! There isn't even any necessity for accuracy!"

"You haven't heard anything yet," another officer broke in. "Mr. Wright's automobile is powered by a small plant similar to the others. He demonstrated it to us. We could find no fuel tank of any kind, or any other driving mechanism. But with a power plant no bigger than six cubic inches, that car, carrying enough weight to give it traction, outpulled an army tank!"

"And the other test!" said the third excitedly. "He put one of the objects into a replica of a treasury vault. The walls were twelve feet thick, super-reinforced concrete. He controlled it from over a hundred yards away. He . . . he burst that vault! It wasn't an explosion —it was as if some incredibly powerful expansive force inside filled it and flattened the walls from inside. They cracked and split and powdered, and the steel girders and rods came twisting and shearing out like . . . like—*whew!* After that he insisted on seeing you.

We knew it wasn't usual, but he said he has more to say and would say it only in your presence."

The president said gravely, "What is it, Mr. Wright?"

Wright rose, picked up his suitcase, opened it and took out a small cube, about eight inches on a side, made of some light-absorbent red material. Four men edged nervously away from it.

"These gentlemen," he began, "have seen only part of the things this device can do. I'm going to demonstrate to you the delicacy of control that is possible with it." He made an adjustment with a tiny knob on the side of the cube, set it on the edge of the president's desk.

"You have asked me more than once if this is my invention or if I am representing someone. The latter is true. It might also interest you to know that the man who controls this cube is right now several thousand miles from here. He and he alone, can prevent it from detonating now that I—" He pulled his detonator out of the suitcase and pressed a button—"have done this. It will explode the way the one we dropped from the plane did, completely destroying this city and everything in it, in just four hours. It will also explode—" He stepped back and threw a tiny switch on his detonator—"if any moving object comes within three feet of it or if anyone leaves this room but me—it can be compensated for that. If, after I leave, I am molested, it will detonate as soon as a hand is laid on me. No bullets can kill me fast enough to prevent me from setting it off."

The three army men were silent. One of them swiped nervously at the beads of cold sweat on his forehead. The others did not move. The president said evenly:

"What's your proposition?"

"A very reasonable one. My employer does not work in the open, for obvious reasons. All he wants is your agreement to carry out his orders; to appoint the cabinet members he chooses, to throw your influence in any way he dictates. The public—Congress—anyone else—need never know anything about it. I might add that if you agree to this proposal, this 'bomb,' as you call it, will not go off. But you can be sure that thousands of them are planted all over the country. You will never know when you are near one. If you disobey, it means instant annihilation for you and everyone else within three or four square miles.

"In three hours and fifty minutes—that will be at precisely seven o'clock—there is a commercial radio program on Station RPRS. You will cause the announcer, after his station identification, to say 'Agreed.' It will pass unnoticed by all but my employer. There is no use in having me followed; my work is done. I shall never see nor contact my employer again. That is all. Good afternoon, gentlemen!"

Wright closed his suitcase with a businesslike snap, bowed, and left the room. Four men sat staring at the little red cube.

"Do you think he can do all he says?" asked the president.

The three nodded mutely. The president reached for his phone.

There was an eavesdropper to all of the foregoing. Conant, squatting behind his great desk in the vault, where he had his sanctum sanctorum, knew nothing of it. But beside him was the compact bulk of Kidder's radiophone. His presence switched it on, and Kidder, on his island, blessed the day he had thought of that device. He had been meaning to call Conant all morning, but was very hesitant. His meeting with the young engineer Johansen had impressed him strongly. The man was such a thorough scientist, possessed of such complete delight in the work he did, that for the first time in his life Kidder found himself actually wanting to see someone again. But he feared for Johansen's life if he brought him to the laboratory, for Johansen's work was done on the island, and Conant would most certainly have the engineer killed if he heard of his visit, fearing that Kidder would influence him to sabotage the great transmitter. And if Kidder went to the power plant he would probably be shot on sight.

All one day Kidder wrangled with himself, and finally determined to call Conant. Fortunately he gave no signal, but turned up the volume on the receiver when the little red light told him that Conant's transmitter was functioning. Curious, he heard everything that occurred in the president's chamber three thousand miles away. Horrified, he realized what Conant's engineers had done. Built into tiny containers were tens of thousands of power receivers. They had no power of their own, but, by remote control, could draw on any or all of the billions of horsepower the huge plant on the island was broadcasting.

Kidder stood in front of his receiver, speechless. There was nothing he could do. If he devised some means of destroying the power plant, the government would certainly step in and take over the island, and then—what would happen to him and his precious Neoterics?

Another sound grated out of the receiver—a commercial radio program. A few bars of music, a man's voice advertising stratoline fares on the installment plan, a short silence, then:

"Station RPRS, voice of the nation's Capital, District of South Colorado."

The three-second pause was interminable.

"The time is exactly . . . er . . . *agreed*. The time is exactly seven P.M., Mountain Standard Time."

Then came a half-insane chuckle. Kidder had difficulty believing it was Conant. A phone clicked. The banker's voice:

"Bill? All set. Get out there with your squadron and bomb up the island. Keep away from the plant, but cut the rest of it to ribbons. Do it quick and get out of there."

Almost hysterical with fear, Kidder rushed about the room and then shot out the door and across the compound. There were five hundred innocent workmen in barracks a quarter mile from the plant. Conant didn't need them now, and he didn't need Kidder. The only safety for anyone was in the plant itself, and Kidder wouldn't leave his Neoterics to be bombed. He flung himself up the stairs and to the nearest teletype. He banged out, "Get me a defense. I want an impenetrable shield. Urgent!"

The words ripped out from under his fingers in the functional script of the Neoterics. Kidder didn't think of what he wrote, didn't really visualize the thing he ordered. But he had done what he could. He'd have to leave them now, get to the barracks; warn those men. He ran up the path toward the plant, flung himself over the white line that marked death to those who crossed it.

A squadron of nine clip-winged, mosquito-nosed planes rose out of a cove on the mainland. There was no sound from the engines, for there were no engines. Each plane was powered with a tiny receiver and drew its unmarked, light-absorbent wings through the air with power from the island. In a matter of minutes they raised the island. The squadron leader spoke briskly into a microphone.

"Take the barracks first. Clean 'em up. Then work south."

Johansen was alone on a small hill near the center of the island. He carried a camera, and though he knew pretty well that his chances of ever getting ashore again were practically nonexistent, he liked angle shots of his tower, and took innumerable pictures. The first he knew of the planes was when he heard their whining dive over the barracks. He stood transfixed, saw a shower of bombs hurtle down and turn the barracks into a smashed ruin of broken wood, metal and bodies. The picture of Kidder's earnest face flashed into his mind. Poor little guy—if they ever bombed his end of the island he would—But his tower! Were they going to bomb the plant?

He watched, utterly appalled, as the planes flew out to sea, cut back and dove again. They seemed to be working south. At the third dive he was sure of it. Not knowing what he could do, he nevertheless turned and ran toward Kidder's place. He rounded a turn in the trail and collided violently with the little biochemist. Kidder's face was scarlet with exertion, and he was the most terrified-looking object Johansen had ever seen.

Kidder waved a hand northward. "Conant!" he

screamed over the uproar. "It's Conant! He's going to kill us all!"

"The plant?" said Johansen, turning pale.

"It's safe. He won't touch *that!* But . . . my place . . . what about all those men?"

"Too late!" shouted Johansen.

"Maybe I can— Come on!" called Kidder, and was off down the trail, heading south.

Johansen pounded after him. Kidder's little short legs became a blur as the squadron swooped overhead, laying its eggs in the spot where they had met.

As they burst out of the woods, Johansen put on a spurt, caught up with the scientist and knocked him sprawling not six feet from the white line.

"Wh . . . wh—"

"Don't go any farther, you fool! Your own damned force field—it'll kill you!"

"Force field? But—I came through it on the way up —Here. Wait. If I can—" Kidder began hunting furiously about in the grass. In a few seconds he ran up to the line, clutching a large grasshopper in his hand. He tossed it over. It lay still.

"See?" said Johansen. "It—"

"Look! It jumped! Come on! I don't know what went wrong, unless the Neoterics shut it off. They generated that field—I didn't."

"Neo—huh?"

"Never mind," snapped the biochemist, and ran.

They pounded gasping up the steps and into the Neoterics' control room. Kidder clapped his eyes to a telescope and shrieked in glee. "They've done it! They've done it!"

"Who's—"

"My little people! The Neoterics! They've made the impenetrable shield! Don't you see—it cut through the lines of force that start up that field out there. Their generator is still throwing it up, but the vibrations can't get out! They're safe! They're safe!" And the overwrought hermit began to cry. Johansen looked at him pityingly and shook his head.

"Sure—your little men are all right. But we aren't,"

he added as the floor shook to the detonation of a bomb.

Johansen closed his eyes, got a grip on himself and let his curiosity overcome his fear. He stepped to the binocular telescope, gazed down it. There was nothing there but a curved sheet of gray material. He had never seen a gray quite like that. It was absolutely neutral. It didn't seem soft and it didn't seem hard, and to look at it made his brain reel. He looked up.

Kidder was pounding the keys of a teletype, watching the blank yellow tape anxiously.

"I'm not getting through to them," he whimpered. "I don't know what's the mat—Oh, of *course!*"

"What?"

"The shield is absolutely impenetrable! The teletype impulses can't get through or I could get them to extend the screen over the building—over the whole island! There's *nothing* those people can't do!"

"He's crazy," Johansen muttered. "Poor little—"

The teletype began clicking sharply. Kidder dove at it, practically embraced it. He read off the tape as it came out. Johansen saw the characters, but they meant nothing to him.

"Almighty," Kidder read falteringly, "pray have mercy on us and be forbearing until we have said our say. Without orders we have lowered the screen you ordered us to raise. We are lost, O great one. Our screen is truly impenetrable, and so cut off your words on the word machine. We have never, in the memory of any Neoteric, been without your word before. Forgive us our action. We will eagerly await your answer."

Kidder's fingers danced over the keys. "You can look now," he gasped. "Go on—the telescope!"

Johansen, trying to ignore the whine of sure death from above, looked.

He saw what looked like land—fantastic fields under cultivation, a settlement of some sort, factories, and— beings. Everything moved with incredible rapidity. He couldn't see one of the inhabitants except as darting pinky-white streaks. Fascinated, he stared for a long minute. A sound behind him made him whirl. It was Kidder, rubbing his hands together briskly. There was a broad smile on his face.

"They did it," he said happily. "You see?"

Johansen didn't see until he began to realize that there was a dead silence outside. He ran to a window. It was night outside—the—blackest night—when it should have been dusk. "What happened?"

"The Neoterics," said Kidder, and laughed like a child. "My friends downstairs there. They threw up the impenetrable shield over the whole island. We can't be touched now!"

And at Johansen's amazed questions, he launched into a description of the race of beings below them.

Outside the shell, things happened. Nine airplanes suddenly went dead-stick. Nine pilots glided downward, powerless, and some fell into the sea, and some struck the miraculous gray shell that loomed in place of an island; slid off and sank.

And ashore, a man named Wright sat in a car, half dead with fear, while government men surrounded him, approached cautiously, daring instant death from a now-dead source.

In a room deep in the White House, a high-ranking army officer shrieked, "I can't stand it any more! I can't!" and leaped up, snatched a red cube off the president's desk, ground it to ineffectual litter under his shining boots.

And in a few days they took a broken old man away from the bank and put him in an asylum, where he died within a week.

The shield, you see, was truly impenetrable. The power plant was untouched and sent out its beams; but the beams could not get out, and anything powered from the plant went dead. The story never became public, although for some years there was heightened naval activity off the New England coast. The navy, so the story went, had a new target range out there—a great hemiovoid of gray material. They bombed it and shelled it and rayed it and blasted all around it, but never even dented its smooth surface.

Kidder and Johansen let it stay there. They were happy enough with their researches and their Neoterics. They did not hear or feel the shelling, for the shield was truly impenetrable. They synthesized their food and their light and air from the materials at hand, and they simply didn't care. They were the only survivors of the bombing, with the exception of three poor maimed devils who died soon afterward.

All this happened many years ago, and Kidder and Johansen may be alive today, and they may be dead. But that doesn't matter too much. The important thing is that the great gray shell will bear watching. Men die, but races live. Some day the Neoterics, after innumerable generations of inconceivable advancement, will take down their shield and come forth. When I think of that I feel frightened.

GHOST OF A CHANCE

SHE SAID, "There's something following me!" in a throttled voice, and started to run.

It sort of got me. Maybe because she was so tiny and her hair was so white. Maybe because, white hair and all, she looked so young and helpless. But mostly, I think, because of what she said. "There's something following me." Not "someone." "Something." So I just naturally hauled out after her.

I caught her at the corner, put my hand on her shoulder. She gasped, and shot away from me. "Take it easy, lady," I panted. "I won't let it get you."

She stopped so suddenly that I almost ran her down. We stood looking at each other. She had great big dark eyes that didn't go with her hair at all. I said, "What makes you go dashing around at three o'clock in the morning?"

"What makes you ask?" Her voice was smooth, musical.

"Now, look—you started this conversation."

She started to speak, and then something over my shoulder caught her eye. She froze for a second: and I was so fascinated by the play of expression on her face that I didn't follow her gaze. Abruptly she brought her eyes back to my face and then slapped it. It was a stinger. I stepped back and swore, and by the time I was finished she was halfway up the block. I stood there rubbing my cheek and let her go.

I met Henry Gade a couple of days later and told him about it. Henry is a practical psychologist. Perhaps I should say his field is practical psychology, because Henry ain't practical. He has theories. He has more damn theories than any man alive. He is thirty

64

and bald and he makes lots of money without doing any work.

"I think she was crazy," I said.

"Ah," said Henry, and laid a finger beside his nose. I think the nose was longer. "But did you ask her what *she* thought?"

"No. I only asked her what she was doing running around that time of night."

"The trouble with you, Gus, is that you have no romance in you. What you should have done was to catch her up in your arms and smothered her with kisses."

"She'd have sla—"

"She did, anyway, didn't she?" said Henry, and walked off.

Henry kids a lot. But he sometimes says crazy things like that when he isn't kidding a bit.

I met the girl again three months later. I was in the Duke's beer garden looking at his famous sunflower. The sunflower was twelve feet tall and had crutches to keep it standing up. It grew beside the dirt alley that was the main road of the beer garden. There were ratty-looking flowerbeds all over the place and tables set among them. And Japanese lanterns that had been out in the rain, and a laryngitic colored band. The place was crowded, and I was standing there letting all that noise beat me back and forth, looking at the sunflower. The Duke swore he could fill a No. 6 paper bag with the seeds from that one flower.

And then she said, "Hello. I'm sorry I had to slap your face." She was squinched up against the stem of the sunflower, in amongst all those shadows and leaves.

I said, "Well, if it isn't my pretty little pug. What do you mean, you're sorry you *had* to? You should be just sorry you did."

"Oh, I had to. I wouldn't slap you just for nothing."

"Oh—I did something? I shoulda got slapped?"

"Please," she said. "I am sorry."

I looked at her. She was. "What are you doing in there—hiding?"

She nodded.

"Who are you hiding from?"

She wouldn't say. She just shrugged and said she was just—you know—hiding.

"Is it the same thing you were running away from that night?"

"Yes."

I told her she was being silly. "I looked all around after you left and there wasn't a thing on the street."

"Oh, yes there was!"

"Not that I could see."

"I know that."

I suddenly got the idea that this was a very foolish conversation. "Come out of there and have a beer with me. We'll talk things over."

"Oh, I couldn't do that!"

"Sure you could. Easy. Look." I reached in and grabbed her.

"You should know better than that," she said, and then something happened to break the stem of the big sunflower. It tottered and came crashing down like a redwood. The huge flower landed on the tray that Giuseppe, the waiter, was carrying. It held eight long beers, two pitchers and a Martini. The beers and a lot of broken glass flew in every direction but up. The Martini went back over his head and crashed on the bars of the cage where the Duke kept his trained squirrel. There was some confusion. The girl with the white hair was gone. All the time that the Duke was telling me what a menace I was, I kept staring over his heaving shoulder at the squirrel, which was lapping up the Martini that had splashed inside the cage. After the Duke ran out of four-letter words he had me thrown out. We'd been pretty good friends before that, too.

I got hold of Henry as soon as I could. "I saw that girl again," I told him, "and I grabbed her like you said." I told him what had happened. He laughed at me. Henry always laughs at me.

"Don't look so solemn about it, Gus!" he said, and slapped me on the back. "A little excitement is good for the blood. Laugh it off. The Duke didn't sue you, did he?"

"No," I said, "not exactly. But that squirrel of his

ate the olive out of that cocktail that fell into his cage
and got awful sick. And the Duke went and had the
doctor send his bill to me. Stomach pump."

Henry had been eating salted nuts, and when I said
that he snorted half a mouthful of chewed nuts up
into his nose. I've done that and it hurts. In a way I
was glad to see Henry suffer.

"I need some help," I told him after he got his
health back. "Maybe that girl's crazy, but I think she's
in trouble."

"She most certainly is," said Henry. "But I don't see
what you could do about it."

"Oh, I'd figure out something."

"I also don't see why you want to help her out."

"That's a funny thing," I said slowly. "You know
me, Henry—I got no use for wimmen unless they leave
me alone. Every time one of 'em does something nice,
it's because she's figgerin' to pull something lousy a
little later."

Henry swallowed some cashews carefully and then
laughed. "You've summed up at least seven volumes
of male objectivism," he said. "But what has that got
to do with your silver-haired Nemesis?"

"Nemesis? I thought maybe she was Polish. Her?
Well, she's never done anything to me that wasn't
lousy. So I figure maybe she's different. I figure maybe
she's going to work it the other way around and pull
something nice. And I want to be around when that
happens."

"Your logic is labored but dependable." He said
something else, about what's the use of being intelli-
gent and educated when all wisdom rests on the lips
of a child of nature, but I didn't catch on. "Well, I'm
rather interested in whether or not you can do anything for her. Go ahead and stick your neck out."

"I don't know where she lives or nothing."

"Oh—that." He pulled out a little notebook and a
silver pencil and wrote down something. "Here," he
said, tearing it off and handing it to me. It said, "Iola
Harvester, 2336 Dungannon Street."

"Who's this?"

"Your damsel in distress. Your dark-eyed slapper of faces."

"How the devil do you know her name?"

"She was a patient of mine for quite a while."

"She was? Why you son-of-a-gun! Why didn't you tell me?"

"Why didn't you ask me?"

I started for the door, reading over the name and address. "You know what, Henry?"

"What?"

"Iola's a pretty name."

Henry laughed. "Let me know how you make out."

I went up and rang the bell. It was a big apartment house; Iola lived on the fourth floor. The foyer door belched at me and I pushed it open and went in. They had one of those self-service elevators so I went up the stairs. Those things make me nervous.

She was waiting up on her floor to find out who had rung the bell. She was wearing a black housecoat that touched the floor all the way around and was close around her throat. It had a stiff collar that stuck up and out and seemed to sort of cradle her head. There was a zipper all down the front and two silver initials on the left breast. I couldn't get my wind right away and it wasn't the stairs.

"Oh!" she said. "It's you!"

"*Yup!*" I looked at her for a minute. "Gee! I didn't know you were so *tiny!*" There was something about her that made me want to laugh out loud, but not because I saw anything funny. When I said that she got pink.

"I . . . don't know whether I should ask you in," she said. "I don't even know your name."

"My name is Gus. So now you can ask me in."

"You're the only man I have ever met who can be fresh without being fresh," she said, and stood aside. I didn't know what she meant, but I went in, anyway. It was a nice place. Everything in it was delicate and small, like Iola. I stood in the middle of the floor spinning my hat on one finger until she took it away from me. "Sit down," she said. I did and she did, with the room between us. "What brings you here; how did you find out my address, and will you have some coffee or a drink?"

"I came because I think you're in a jam and you might need help. A friend of mine gave me your name and address. I don't want any coffee and what have you got to drink?"

"Sauterne," she said. "Rum, rye and Scotch."

"I never *touch* that stuff."

"What do you drink?"

"Gin." She looked startled. "Or milk. Got any milk?"

She had. She got me a great big glass of it. She even had some herself. She said, "Now, whats on your mind?"

"There's nothing you can do."

"Oh, yes there is. There must be. If you'll tell me what's botherin' you, making you hide away in . . . in sunflowers and runnin' away from nothing. I'll bet I could fix you up—What are you laughing at?"

"You're so earnest!" she said.

"Everybody's all the time laughing at me," I said sadly. "Well, how about it?"

The smile faded away from her face and she sat for a long time saying nothing. I went and sat beside her and looked at her. I didn't try to touch her at all. Suddenly she nodded and began to talk.

"I might as well tell you. It's tough to keep it to myself. Most people would laugh at me; the one doctor I went to eventually gave me up as a bad job. He said I was kidding myself. He said that what had happened just couldn't happen—I imagined it all. But you—I think I can trust you. I don't know why—

"It started about two years ago. I had a slight crush on a fellow at a summer camp. He took me to a dance one night—one of those country square dances. It was a lot of fun and we danced ourselves tired. Then we went out onto the lake shore and he—well, the moon and all, you know—he put his arms around me. And just then a voice spoke to me. It said, 'If you know what's good for you, you'll keep away from this fellow.' I started back and asked the boy if he had said something. He hadn't. I was scared and ran all the way home. He tried to catch me, but he couldn't. I saw him the next day and tried to apologize but there wasn't very much I could say. I tried to be nice to him, but as time went on he got more and more irritable. And he lost weight. He wound up in the hospital. Almost—died. You see, he couldn't sleep. He was afraid to sleep. He had the most terrible dreams. I heard about one of them. It was awful.

"I didn't realize then that my seeing him had anything to do with his getting sick; but as soon as they had him in the hospital he began to get better, fast, as long as I didn't visit him. Then he would have a relapse. I heard that after he left the camp for good and went back to his home in Chicago, he was quite all right.

"Well, nothing happened for quite a while, and then I began to notice that a counterman at a sandwich bar where I ate every day had begun to act strangely. I saw him every day, but there was absolutely nothing between us. One afternoon while I was eating, he began dropping things. It was nothing at first, but it got very bad. It got so that he couldn't lift so much as a spoon without dropping it. He spilled cup after cup of coffee. He would try to make a sandwich and he'd drop the makings all over the floor and his work table. He couldn't set a place at the counter, he couldn't wait on anybody—*as long as I was there!* At first he kidded about it and called me his jinx girl. But after a week or so of that, he came over to me just as I sat down and said:

"'Miss Harvester, I hope you don't mind what I'm going to say, but something's got to be done. I'll lose my job if I don't stop dropping things. But I never do that unless you're here! I don't know why it is, but there you have it. Would you be angry if I asked you not to eat here for a while? I was astonished, but he was so worried and so polite about it that I never ate there again. And from what I've heard my friends say, he never dropped anything again.

"And from then on it got worse and worse. A traffic cop, a nice old man, that I used to nod to each morning on my way to work, began to *itch!* I could see it, every time I passed him! I'd nod, and he'd nod, and then start to scratch as if he itched so badly he just couldn't help himself. And an office boy who spent a lot of time near my desk began to miss doors! I mean, he just couldn't get through a door without running into the jamb. The poor boy almost went crazy. He'd walk slowly toward a door, aim carefully, and try to go through, but he couldn't do it unless he struck the jamb first. I got so heartsick watching him that I quit my job and got another—which took care of the nice policeman, too. Neither of them were ever troubled again.

"But that's the way it's been ever since. Any man I see regularly starts suffering dreadfully from some strange trouble. It's bad enough for the ones who just see me in a routine way. But oh, the poor men who try to take me out to shows and things! When I go out, that strange voice speaks to me again, and tells me to keep away from the man. And if I don't, he gets terribly sick, or he gets blind spells when he crosses any streets, or he does things that cause him to lose his job or his business. Do you see what I'm up against?"

"Don't cry, Miss Iola. Please don't cry."

"I'm n-not crying, Mr. Gus!"

"Just plain Gus!"

"Well then, you call me just plain Iola. Or Miss Harvester. Not Miss Iola."

"I'd have to feel a certain way about you to call you Iola," I said slowly. "And I'd have to feel a certain other way about you to call you Miss Harvester. I'm goin' to call you Miss Iola."

"Oh, Gus," she said, "you're so *cute!*" She smiled and sipped some milk and then went on with her story.

"I work now for a woman who owns a cosmetic business," she said. "I have a woman boss and a woman manager and office force and mostly women customers. And I hate them! I hate all women!"

"Me, too," I said.

She gave me an odd glance, and went on. "Once in a while I'm free of this thing. I can't tell you exactly how I know, but I do. It's a sort of lightening of pressure. And then I'll be walking along the street and I can feel it trying to catch up with me—just as if it had hunted me out and was following me. Sometimes I can hide and get away from it. Generally I can't."

"Oh—that's why you were running away that night I first saw you! But—why did you slap my face?"

"Because I liked you."

"That's a funny sort of way to show it, Miss Iola."

"Oh, no! The thing, whatever it is, had just caught up with me. It knew I liked you. It would have done some terrible thing to you if I hadn't slapped you to make it think I disliked you. And after I had done it I was so ashamed I ran away."

"Why did you break the stem of the sunflower?"

"Gus, I didn't! The thing did that, to get you in trouble."

"He succeeded."

"Oh, Gus—I'm so sorry."

"What for? Not your fault."

"Not—Gus, you believe me, don't you?"

She kissed me. Just a little one, on the cheek, but it made my heart pop up into the back of my neck and slug me.

"Well," I said as soon as I could make my breathing operate my voice, "whatever this thing is, I'll help you lick it. Ah—what is it, by the way? Got any ideas?"

"Yes," she said quietly. "I certainly have. When I told the doctor this, it convinced him that I was suffering from an overdose of old wives' tales. Doesn't it seem funny to you that after all I've told you about what happens to a man if I so much as talk to him, nothing is happening to you?"

"Come to think of it, it is funny."

"Look, then," she said, pointing. "There, and there, and there!"

I looked. Over the tops of the three doors that opened into the room, and over the two big windows, were strands of—garlic.

"I . . . heard of that," I said. "A ghost, huh?"

"A ghost," said Iola. "A jealous ghost. A dirty,

rotten dog-in-the-manger ghost! Why doesn't he leave me alone?"

"I'll tear'm apart," I growled.

She smiled, the saddest, puckered-up little smile I ever did see. "No, Gus, no. You're strong, all right, but that kind of strength won't do me much good with my haunt."

"I'll find some way, Miss Iola," I said. "I will, so help me!"

"You'll try," she said softly. "So help *me!*"

She got my hat and opened the door for me, then closed it with a bang, whirled and stood with her back to it. "Gus!" She was pale, anyway, but now she looked bloodless. "Gus. He's out there! The ghost—he knows you're in here, and he's waiting for you!"

I looked at my hands. "Move on out of the way, then, Miss Iola," I said quietly, "and let me at him."

"No, Gus—no!"

"Now, looky here. It's getting late—too late for you to have my kind in your digs. I'll run along." I walked over to her, took her by the shoulders, and lifted her out of the way. Her forehead was near, so I kissed it before I put her down.

"Good night," I said. She didn't answer. She was crying, so I guess she couldn't. Awful scared. I was glad about that because I knew it wasn't herself she was scared for.

I woke up the next morning and thought I was still asleep, in the middle of a foul dream. I was cold—stone-cold, wet-cold. I felt as slimy as an eel in a barrel of oil. I opened my eyes and tried to shake the feeling off. It wouldn't shake. My last night's dinner rolled inside me as I realized that the sliminess was there, all right—my two sheets were coated with it. I could feel the wet, thick mass of it all over me. I could strip it off one arm with the other hand, and throw it —*sclup*—onto the floor.

But I couldn't see it.

I ran, gasping and retching, into the bathroom. My feet seemed to slip on the stuff, and I had trouble turning the doorknob with my slimy fingers. I climbed under the hottest shower I had ever taken, soaped, rinsed, soaped again, rinsed again. And I got out of the tub feeling cold and clammy and slimy as ever.

I tried to put some clothes on, but I couldn't stand the pressure of them; they seemed to drive the thick mass of it into my pores. I threw them off, leaped into bed, and pulled the covers over me, and with a yelp I leaped out again. It was bad enough to have it, but I couldn't bear to wallow in it. The phone rang. Iola.

"Gus, I'm terribly worried about you. Has he . . . it . . . done anything to you?"

I hesitated. It wouldn't do any good to lie. "Yeah, he's been skylarking around."

"Gus, what has he done?"

"Nothin' worth talking about."

"Oh, you won't tell me. It must be something really terrible!"

"Why so?"

"Because I . . . I . . . well, I—Gus, aren't you going to say it first? Why is it that he would treat you worse than any other man?"

I slowly began to get what she was driving at. "Miss Iola—you don't lo . . . care for me or something?"

"Darling!"

I said, "Holy smoke!"

I did some thinking after I hung up. I couldn't let this thing get me down—not now, not after my hearing news like that. I clamped my jaw and got out some clean underwear and socks. I was remembering something my pop told me after my first street fight. "If you git hurt, me bye, don't let th' other fellow know it. If he thinks he can't hurt ye, ye've got 'im licked."

So I dressed. With my clothes I clasped the chill ooze to me, and when I walked out the door the slime dripped from the creases of my flesh as I moved. I stepped out onto the street with some misgivings, but it was invisible, thank the Powers.

And when I woke the next day the sliminess was gone.

I went to Henry Gade's place and borrowed a pen and paper. I had told him what I'd heard from Iola about her trouble, but nothing else.

"Who are you writing to?" he asked over his pipe,

watching me scratching laboriously away at the letter.

"I'm doin' what anyone should do when he's in trouble—consulting an expert," I said, and kept on writing.

"'Miss Beatrice Dix, *The Daily Mail*,'" he read aloud, and roared with laughter. "So you've got trouble along those lines, too, have you? Ha? Beatrice Dix —Advice to the Lovelorn!"

"You tell your little mouth to stop making those noises or it'll get poked," I growled. He went on reading what I had written:

Dear Miss Dix:

I got a problem about a girl I am very serious with. This girl has a fellow who likes her, but she don't like him none at all. He keeps on bothering her and ordering her to keep away from other men, but he never comes to see her or gives her anything or takes her out and on top of that he keeps on doing things to any other man that is interested in her and especially to me because—

"Good heavens, Gus, couldn't you put a full stop in there somewhere?"

—because I am at present her big moment. The things he does are not the kind of things you can get the law on him for. What I want to know is what right has this fellow to be so jealous when the girl has no use for him and what can we do to get rid of him.

"Either you're an extremely exacting student of literary styling," said Henry, "or you actually are the kind of person who writes in to Beatrice Dix's column. I've always wondered what one of those nitwits looked like," he added thoughtfully, standing off and regarding me as if I were a museum piece. "Tell me—who's the cutter-inner in your little romance?"

"A ghost."

"A ghost? Iola's jealous ghost? Gus, Gus, you improve by the hour. And do you really think you can exorcise him with the aid of a heart-throb column?"

"He don't need no exercise."

"Get out of here, Gus, you're killing me."

"I will before I do," I said.

The following day Iola's haunt created something new and different for me. But I couldn't brave this one out. I stayed home all day after phoning the boss that I was very, very ill. Exactly what was done couldn't be printed.

The answer to my letter came far sooner than I had hoped. I hadn't asked for a personal reply, and so it was printed, with my letter, thus:

G. S.:

You are up against a very difficult problem, if we understand the situation correctly. We have run up against such cases before. The young man who is persecuting the two of you will continue to do so just as long as he finds the girl attractive to his peculiar type of mind. And what can you do about it?

You can ignore him completely.

Or you can, together or singly, get the man to talk the whole thing out with you.

Or you might try to find someone else who would interest him.

But you must be patient. Please, for your own sakes, do not do anything rash.

I read it over half a dozen times. I figured this Dix woman was a real expert at this racket, and she ought to know what to do. But how about it? "Ignore him completely." How can you be married to a woman when you know you're liable to turn slimy at a moment's notice? "Appeal to his better nature—talk it out with him." Catch him first. "Find someone else who would interest him." Catch a lady ghost, huh? And persuade her to vamp him.

I took the paper over to Henry Gade. He's better at thinking things out than I am.

He waved the paper aside as I came in. "I've seen it," he said. "I was looking for it."

"What do you think?"

"I think it's a lovely piece of say-nothing, except

that she hit the nail on the head when she said that the guy will keep right on bothering you lovebirds just as long as he finds the girl attractive. I can't get over it!" he exploded, and put his head on one side, watching me. "Good old Gus, in love after all these years!"

"Maybe it hits harder for that," I said, and he stopped his ape-grinning and laid a hand on my shoulder.

"I guess it does. You do reach in and get the truth at times, old man."

The letter from Iola was waiting for me when I got back home.

Dearest Gus,

This is a rotten thing for me to do, but I've got to do it. I have a suspicion of what you've been going through so bravely; he talked to me last night and told me some of the things he's done to you.

So you mustn't write, Gus darling, and you mustn't phone, and above all you must never, never see me again. It's the only way out for both of us, and if it's a painful and a cruel way, then that's the breaks.

But, beloved—don't try to get in touch with me. I have bought a little revolver, and if you do that I'll kill myself. That's not idle talk, Gus. I'm not afraid to do it. I've lived through enough pain.

Sweet, sweet sweetheart, how my heart bleeds for you!

I read it over once and tried to read it again because, somehow, I couldn't see so well. Then I dove for the phone, and thought about the revolver, and turned my back on it. Oh, she'd do it—I knew her.

Then I went out.

Henry found me. Maybe it was three weeks later, maybe four. I didn't know because I didn't give a damn. I was sitting on a bench with a couple of other gentlemen.

"Go away. You're Henry. I remember you. Go away, Henry."

"Gus! Get up out of that! You're drunk! Come home with me, Gus."

One of the other gentlemen back-slid to the extent of taking some of Henry's money for helping Henry get me home. Once there, I slept the clock around.

Henry woke me, sponging my face with warm water. "Lost thirty pounds or more," he was muttering. "Filthy rags—ten-day beard—"

"You know what happened to me," I said, as if that excused and explained everything.

"Yes, I know what happened to you," he roared. "You lost your cotton-headed filly. And did you stand up and take it? No! You lay down and let yourself get kicked like the jelly-bellied no-good you are!"

"But she wouldn't—"

"I know, I know. She refused to see you any more. That's got nothing to do with it. You're wound up with her—finished. And you tried to run away. You tried to escape into filth and rotgut liquor. Don't you realize that you do nothing that way but burn up what's clean in you and leave all that's rotten, with the original wound festering in the middle of it?"

I turned my face to the wall, but I couldn't stop his voice. "Get up and bathe and shave and eat a decent meal! Try to act like a human being until you can give as good an imitation as you used to."

"No," I said thickly.

Suddenly he was on his knees by the bed, an arm across my shoulders. "Stop your blubbering," he said gently. "Gus—you're a grown man now." He sat back on his haunches, frowning and breathing too deeply. Suddenly he rolled me over on my back, began slapping my face with his right hand, back and front, back and front, over and over and over.

And then something snapped inside me and I reared up off the bed and sent a whistling roundhouse at him. He ducked under it and jarred me with a left to the temple. And then we went to work. I was big and emaciated, and he was little and inspired. It was quite a show. It ended with him stretched out on the carpet.

"Thanks, Gus," he grinned weakly.

"Why'd you get me so riled up? Why'd you make me hit you?"

"Applied psychology," he said, getting up groggily. I helped him.

I felt my swollen nose. "I thought psychology was brain stuff!"

"Listen, pal. You and I are going to straighten old Gus out for good. You've got something deep inside that hurts—right? What did you see in that white-headed babe, anyway?"

"She's . . . she's . . . I just can't get along without her."

"You got slushy. I think your taste is lousy." Henry's eyes were narrowed and he teetered on the balls of his feet. He knew when he was treading on thin ice, but he was going through with this. "What do you see in an anaemic-looking wench like that? Give me nice, firm, rosy girls with some blood in their veins. *Heh!* Her, with her white hair and white skin and two great big black holes for eyes. She looks like a ghost! She isn't worth—"

I roared and charged. He stepped nimbly out of the way. I charged right past him and into the bathroom. "Where's your razor?" I shouted. "Where's the soap?" And I dove into the shower.

When I came out of the bathroom and started climbing into some clothes, he demanded an explanation. "What did I say? What did I do?" He was hopping exultantly from one foot to the other.

"You said it a long while back," I said. "So did Beatrice Dix. Something about, 'He'll annoy you just as long as he finds the girl attractive.' " I laced the second shoe, demanded some money, and pounded out before I had the sentence well finished.

I rang somebody else's bell at the apartment house and when the buzzer burped at me I headed for the stairs. I rang Iola's bell and waited breathlessly. The knob turned and I crowded right in. She was drawing a negligee about her. Her eyes were red-rimmed.

"Gus!" She drew back, turned and ran to a lamp table. "Oh, you *fool!* Why do you have to make it harder for us?" She moved so fast I couldn't stop her. She had the gun in her hand.

"Hold on, you little dope!" I roared. "That may be

a way out, but you're not going out alone. We're going together!"

"Gus—"

"And doing it together we're not doing it that way! Give me that thing!" I strode across the room, lifted it out of her hand. I opened the magazine, took the barrel in one hand and the butt in the other and twisted them apart, throwing the pieces at her feet. "Now get in there and get dressed. We've got things to do!" She hesitated, and I pushed her roughly toward the bedroom. "One of us is going to dress you," I said somberly.

She squeaked and moved. I tramped up and down the living room, gleefully kicking the broken gun on every trip. She was ready in about four minutes; she came out frightened and puzzled and radiant. I took her wrist and dragged her out of the apartment. As soon as we passed under the garlic on the door, my skin began to tingle, then to itch, and suddenly I felt that I was a mass of open, festering sores. And on top of this came the slime again. I gritted my teeth and sluiced down my pain with sheer exultation.

We piled into a taxi and I gave an address. When Iola asked questions I laughed happily. We pulled up at a curb and I paid off the driver. "Go on in there," I said.

"A beauty parlor! But what—"

I pushed her in. A white-uniformed beautician came forward timidly. I took a strand of Iola's white hair and tossed it. "Dye this," I said. "Dye it black!"

"Gus!" gasped Iola. "You're mad! I don't *want* to be a brunette! I haven't the coloring for—"

"Coloring? You know what kind of coloring you have, with those big black holes of eyes and that white skin and hair? *You look like a ghost!* Don't you see? That's why he hounded you! That's why he loved you and was jealous of you!"

Her eyes got very bright. She looked in a mirror and said, "Gus—you remember that summer I told you about, when he first spoke to me? I was wearing a long white dress—white shoes—"

"Get in there and be a brunette," I growled. The operator took her.

I settled down into a big chair to wait. I was suffering a thousand different agonies, a hundred different kinds of torments. Pains and horrid creeping sensations flickered over my body the way colors shift on a color-organ. I sat there taking it, and taking it, and then I heard the operator's voice from the back of the studio. "There you are, ma'am. All done. Look in there—how do you like it?"

And deep within me I almost heard a sound like a snort of disgust, and then there was a feeling like an infinite lightening of pressure. And then my body was fresh and whole again, and the ghostly pains were gone.

Iola came out and flung her arms around my neck. As a brunette she was stunning.

Henry Gade was our best man.

PRODIGY

MAYB, CHIEF Guardian for the Third Sector of the Crèche, writhed in her sleep. She pressed her grizzled head into the mattress, and her face twisted. She was deep in slumber, but slumber could not keep out the niggling, soundless, insistent pressure that had slipped into her mind. Sleep was as futile a guard as the sheet which she instinctively pulled up about her ears.

"Mayb!"

She rolled over, facing the wall, her mind refusing to distinguish between the sound of her name in the annunciator and this other, silent, imperative thing.

"Mayb!"

She opened her eyes, saw on the wall the ruby radiance from the annunciator light, grunted and sat up, wincing as she recognized consciously both summonses. Swinging her legs out of the bed, she leaned forward and threw the toggle on the annunciator. "Yes, Examiner."

The voice was resonant but plaintive. "Can't you do something with that little br—with that Andi child? I need my sleep."

"I'll see what he wants," she said resignedly, "although I *do* think, Examiner, that these midnight attentions are doing him more harm than good. One simply does not cater to children this way."

"This is not an ordinary child," said the speaker unnecessarily. "And I still need my sleep. Do what you can, Mayb. And thank you." The light went out.

There was a time, thought Mayb grumpily, as she pulled on her robe, when I thought I could shield the little demon. I thought I could do something for him. That was before he began to know his own power.

84

She let herself out into the hall. "Subtle," she muttered bitterly. Sector One, where children entered the Crèche at the age of nine months, and Sector Two, into which went those who had not fallen by the wayside in eighteen months of examinations—they were simple. The mutants and the aberrants were easy to detect. The subtlety came in Sector Three, where abnormal metabolisms, undeveloped or nondeveloping limbs or organs, and high-threshold reactive mentalities were weeded out by the time they got there, and behavior, almost alone, was the key to normality.

Mayb loved children, all children—which was one of the most important parts of being a Guardian. When it became necessary for her to recommend a child for Disposal, she sometimes stalled a little, sometimes, after it was done, cried a great deal. But she did it when it had to be done, which was the other part of being a good Guardian. She hadn't been so good with Andi, though. Perhaps the little demon had crawled farther into her affections—at first, anyway—with his unpretty, puckish face and his extraordinary coloring, his toasted gold hair and the eyes that should have belonged to a true redhead. She remembered—though at present it was difficult to recall a tenderness—how she had put aside the first suspicions that he was an Irregular, how she had tried to imagine signs that his infuriating demands were temporary, that some normal behavior might emerge to replace the wild talent for nuisance that he possessed.

On the other hand, she thought as she shuffled down the hall, it may seem hardhearted of me, but things like this justify the Code of the Norm. Things like this can be remembered when we have to send some completely endearing little moppet into the Quiet Room, to await the soft hiss of gas and the chute to the incinerator.

Mayb reacted violently to the thought, and wondered, shaking, whether she was getting calloused in her old age, whether she was turning a personal resentment on the child because of this personal inconvenience. She shook off the thought, and for a moment tried not to think at all. Then came the shadow of a wish for the early days of the Normalcy program, two centuries before. That must have been wonderful. Normalcy came first. The children went into the crèches for observation, and were normal or were disposed of. Homo superior could wait. It was humanity's only choice; restore itself to what it had been before the Fourth War—a mammal which could predictably breed true—or face a future of battles between mutations which, singly and in groups, would fight holy wars on the basis of "What I am is normal."

And now, though the idea behind the program was still the same, and the organizations of the crèches were still the same, a new idea was gaining weight daily—to examine Irregulars always more meticulously, with a view, perhaps, to letting one live—one which might benefit all of humanity by his very difference; one who might be a genius, a great artist in some field, or who might have a phenomenal talent for organizing or some form of engineering. It was the thin end of the wedge for Homo superior, who would, by definition, be an Irregular. Irregulars, however, were not necessary Homo superior, and the winnowing process could be most trying. As with Andi, for example.

Holding her breath, she opened the door of his cubicle. As she did so the light came on and the ravening emanation from the child stopped. He rose up from his bed like a little pink seal and knelt, blinking at her, in the middle of the bed.

"Now, what do you want?"

"I want a drink of water and a plastibubble and go swimmin' " said the four-year-old.

"Now Andi," Mayb said, not unkindly, "there's water right here in your room. The plastibubbles have all been put away and it isn't *time* for swimming. Why can't you be a good boy and sleep like all the other children?"

"I am NOT like the uvver children," he said emphatically. "I want a plastibubble."

Mayb sighed, and pulled out an old, old psychological trick. "Which would you like—a drink of water or a plastibubble?" As she spoke she slid her foot onto the pedal of the drinking fountain in the corner of the tiny room. The water gurgled enticingly. Before he was well aware of what he was doing, Andi was out of bed and slurping up the water, with the cancelation of his want for the plastibubble taking root in his mind.

"It tas-tuz better when you push the pedal," he said charmingly.

"Well, that's sweet of you, Andi. But did you know I was fast asleep and had to get up and come here to do it?"

"Thass all right," said Andi blandly.

She turned to the door as he climbed back on the bed. "I wanna go swimmin'."

"No one goes swimming at night!"

"Fishes do."

"You're not a fish."

"Well, ducks, then."

"You're not—" No; this could go on all night. "You go to sleep, young fellow."

"Tell me a story."

"Now, Andi, this isn't story telling time. I told you a story before bedtime."

"You tol' it to everybody. Now tell it to _me_."

"I'm sorry, Andi; this isn't the time," she said firmly. She touched the stud which would switch the light off when she closed the door. "Shut your eyes, now, and have a nice dream. Good night, Andi."

She closed the door, shaking her head and yawning. And instantly that soundless, pressurized command began yammering out, unstoppable, unanswerable. Telepathy was not a novelty nowadays, with the welter of mutations which had reared their strange, unviable heads since the Fourth War; but this kind of thing was beyond belief. It was unbearable. Mayb could sense the Examiner rearing up on his bed, clapping his hands uselessly over his ears, and swearing volubly. She opened the door. "Andi!"

"Well, tell me a story."

"No, Andi!"

He rolled over with his face to the wall. She could see him tensing his body. At the first wave of fury from him she cried out and struck herself on the temples. "All right, all right! What story do you want to hear?"

"Tell me about the bear and the liger."

She sat down wearily on the bed. He hunkered up with his back to the wall, his strange auburn eyes round and completely, unmercifully, awake.

"Lie down and I'll tell you."

"I do-wanna."

"Andi," she said sternly. For once it worked. He lay down. She covered up his smooth pink body, tucking the sheet-blanket carefully around him in the way she sometimes did for the others at bedtime. It was a deft operation, soothing, suggesting warmth and quiet and, above all, sleep. It did nothing of the kind for Andi.

"Once upon a time there was a bear who was bare because his mother was radioactive," she began, "and one day he was walking along beside a neon mine, when a liger jumped out. Now a liger is half lion and half tiger. And *he* said,

" 'Hey, you, bear; you have no hair;
You're not normal; get away there!'

"And the bear said,

'You chase me, liger, at your peril
You're not normal because you're sterile.'

"So they began to fight. The liger fought the bear because he thought it was right to be natural-born, even if he couldn't have babies. And the bear fought the liger because he thought it was right to be what he was as long as he could have babies, even if his mother was radioactive. So they fought and they fought until they killed each other dead. And *that* was because they were both wrong.

"And then from out of the rocks around the neon mine came a whole hundred lemmings. And they frisked and played around the dead bear and the dead liger, and they bred, and pretty soon they had their babies, a thousand of them, and they all lived and grew fat. And do you know why?"

"What was they?"

"Lemmings. Well, they——"

"I want some lemonade," said Andi.

Mayb threw up her hands in exasperation. You can't cure an Irregular by indoctrination, she thought. She said, "I haven't finished. You see, the lemmings lived because their babies were the same as *they* were. That's called breeding true. They were Nor—"

"You know what I'd do if I was a bear without any hair?" Andi shouted, popping up from under the covers. "I'd rear back at that old liger and I'd say don't touch me, you. I hate you and you can't touch me." A wave of emotion from the child nearly knocked Mayb off the bed. "If you come near me. I'll make your brains FRY!" and with the last syllable he loosed a flood of psychic force that made Mayb grunt as if she had walked into the end of an I-beam in the dark.

Andi lay down again and gave her a sweet smile. "Thass what I'd do," he said gently.

"My!" said Mayb. She rose and backed off from him as if he were loaded with high explosive. The movement was quite involuntary.

"You can go away now," said Andi.

"All right. Good night, Andi."

"You better hurry, you ol' liger, you," he said, raising himself on one elbow.

She hurried. Outside, she leaned against the door jamb, sweating profusely. She waited tensely for some further sign from within the cubicle, and when there was none after minutes, she heaved a vast sigh of relief and started back to her bed. This was the third time this week, and the unscheduled nightwork made her feel every one of her twenty-eight years of service to the Crèche. Fuming and yawning, she composed herself for what was left of her night's sleep.

"Mayb!"

She twitched in her sleep. *Not again,* said her subconscious. *Oh, not again. Send him to the Quiet Room and have done with it.* Again she made the futile, unconscious gesture of pulling the covers over her head.

"Mayb! Mayb!"

The annunciator light seemed fainter now, like the slight blush of a pale person. Mayb lowered the covers from her face and looked at the wall, blinked, and sat upright with a squeal. Her eye fell on the clock; she had to look three times to believe what it told her. "Oh no, oh no," she said, and threw the toggle. "Yes Examiner. Oh, I'm so *sorry!* I overslept, and it's three whole hours. Oh, what shall I do?"

"That part's all right," said the speaker. "I had your gong disconnected. You needed the sleep. But you'd better come to my office. Andi's gone."

"Gone? He can't be gone. He was just about to go to sl—oh. *Oh!* The door! I was so distraught when I left him; I must have left the door unl . . . oh-h, Examiner, how awful!"

"It isn't good," said the speaker. "Essie took over for you and she's new and doesn't know all the children. So he wasn't missed until the Free Time when Observation 2 missed him. Well, come on in. We'll see what we can do." The light went out, and the toggle clicked back.

Mayb muttered a little while she dressed. Up the corridor she flew, down a resilient ramp and round to the right, where she burst into the door over which the letters EXAMINER drifted in midair. "Oh dear," she said as she huddled to a stop in the middle of a room which was more lounge than office. "*Dear* oh dear—"

"Poor Mayb." The Examiner was a beaming, tight-skinned pink man with cotton hair. "You've had the worst of this case all along. Don't blame yourself so!"

"What shall we do?"

"Do you know Andi's mother?"

"Yes. Library-Beth."

"Oh, yes," the Examiner nodded. "I was going to look her up and vize her, but I thought perhaps you'd rather."

"Anything, Examiner, anything I can do. Why, that poor little tyke wandering around loose—"

The Examiner laughed shortly. "Think of the poor little people he wanders against. Uh—call her home first."

Mayb went to the corner and wheeled the index to the Library designations, found the number and spoke it into the screen, which lit up. A moment later its blankness dissolved away like windblown fog, to show a young woman's face. She was the true redhead from whom Andi had his eyes, that was certain.

"You remember me," said Mayb. "Crèche-Mayb; I'm Andi's Sector-Guardian."

"Uh-huh," said the woman positively.

"Is . . . is Andi there?"

"Uh-uh," said the woman negatively.

"Now Beth—are you sure?"

The woman wet her lips. "Sure I'm sure. Isn't he locked up in your old crèche? What are you trying to do; trick me again into signing that paper to have him put in the Quiet Room?"

"Why, Beth! No one ever tried to trick you! We just sent you a report and our recommendation."

"I know, I know," said the woman sullenly. "And if I sign it you'll put him away, and if I don't sign it you'll appeal and the Examining Board'll back you up. They always do."

"That's because we're very careful. Guardians—"

"Guardians!" snarled Beth. "What kind of Guardians let a four-year-old child wander out of the Crèche?"

"We are not guardians of the children," said Mayb with sudden dignity, "we are Guardians of the Norm."

"Well you'll never get him back!" screamed Beth. "Never, you hear?" The screen went black.

"Is Andi there?" The Examiner's eyes twinkled.

"My goodness," murmured Mayb. "My, my goodness!"

"I wish those predisposal examinations had never passed the Board. If it weren't for them, this would never have happened. Why, ten years ago we'd have quietly put the little fellow out of the way when we found he was an Irregular. Now we have to wait three weeks, and poke and prod and pry to see if the irregularity can possibly turn into a talent. I tell you, it'll break the crèches. The mother of every last freak on earth is going to cry that her little monster is a genius."

"Oh, if only I hadn't been careless with that silly old door!" She wrung her hands.

"Mayb, don't get worked up. It'll be all right. I'm sure it will."

"You're so nice!" Her voice was shockingly loud in the still room. "Oh dear! Suppose that woman really does hide him? I mean, suppose she takes him away? Do you realize what it will be like if that child is allowed to grow up?"

"Now that is a terrifying thought."

"Think of it! He already knows what he can do, and he's only four years old. Think of those radiations of his grown up man-sized! Suppose he suddenly appeared, grown up, in the middle of a city. Why, when he wanted anything, he'd get it. He'd *have* to get it. And he couldn't be stopped! He can't be reached at all when he does that!"

The Examiner took her arms and gently led her to a mirror on the wall. "Look at yourself, Mayb. You know, you don't look at all like the fine, reliable Guardian you are. Suppose Essie saw you now; you'd never be able to teach her a thing. I'm head of the Crèche. That's a privilege, and there's a certain amount of worrying I have to do to earn it. So let me do the worrying."

"You're so good," she sobbed. "But—I'm *afraid!*"

"I'm afraid, too," he agreed soberly. "It's a bad business. But—don't worry. Tell you what. You just go and lie down for a while. Cry yourself out if you want to—it'll do you good. And then go on with your work." He patted her on the shoulder. "This isn't the end of the world."

"It might be," she gasped, "with creatures like that loose in it, forcing and pressing and pushing and not to be stopped until they had what they wanted."

"Go on now."

She went, wringing her hands.

It was almost exactly the same time the next morning when Mayb was summoned from the Assembly Room where she was teaching her children to sing

"There was a young fellow called Smitti
Who lived in an abnormal city.
His children were bugs

And two-headed slugs,
Oh dear! What a terrible pity!"
and in the midst of the children's shrill merriment at
Smitti's comic predicament she got the Examiner's call.

The thin veil of laughter fell from her face and she
rose. "Free time!" she called. The children took the
signal as a permission to play; the hidden watchers
behind one-way glass in Observation 1 and 2 bent toward their panes, Normalcy Reaction charts at their
elbows.

Mayb hurried to the Examiner's office. She found
him alone rubbing his hands. "Well, Mayb! I knew it
would be all right."

"It's about Andi? You've found him? Did you get
the police?"

"She got them." He laughed. "She got them, herself.
She just couldn't take it—his own mother."

"Where is he?"

"She's bringing him . . . and I'll bet that's her, right
now."

The door swung open. An Under-Guardian said,
"Library-Beth, Examiner."

Pushing past the underling, Library-Beth entered.
Her flaming hair was unkempt; her face was white
and her eyes wild. In her arms she carried the limp
form of Andi.

"Here he is . . . here! Take him; I can't stand it! I
thought I could, but I can't. I didn't know what I was
doing. I'm a good citizen; I want to do my duty; I
care about the law, and the Norm, and the race. I was
crazy, I guess. I had a thing all made up to tell you,
about Andi, about him surviving, that was it—he can
survive better than anyone else on earth, he can; he
can get anything he wants just by wanting it, and no
one can say no to him, not so it makes any difference
to him." It poured from her in a torrent. She put the
limp form down on the settee. "But I didn't know it
was like this. And he badgered me all night and I
couldn't sleep, and he ran away in the morning and I
couldn't find him, and he hated me and when I saw
him and ran to him he hated me with his mind, more
and more and more the nearer I got, so that I couldn't

touch him, and people gathered round and looked at him as if he was a monster, and he is, and he hated them all, every one of them. And somebody got a policeman and he threw sleep-dust, and Andi made a hate then that made everyone cry out and run away, and he hated everyone until he fell asleep. Now take him. Where is that paper? Where is it?"

"Beth, Beth, don't. Please don't. You'll flurry everyone in the place, and all the children."

"Where's the paper?" she screamed, joltingly. It made Mayb's ears ring.

The Examiner went for the form, handed two copies and a stylus to Beth. She signed them, and then collapsed weeping into a chair.

"M-mayb?" The voice was faint.

"He's waking up. Quick, Mayb. Take him to the Quiet Room!"

Mayb scooped up the child and ran, kicking the door open. Two doors down the hall was a cubicle exactly like all the other cubicles, except that it had a black door. And certain concealed equipment. This time she did not forget to press the door until it was locked. Gray with tension, she went back to the office. "All right, Examiner."

The Examiner nodded and stepped swiftly to his button-board. He pressed a certain button firmly, and a red light appeared.

"Andi!" Beth moaned.

Mayb went to her and put her arms around her. "There now. It's for the best. This doesn't happen much any more. We used to have to do it all the time. Soon we'll never have to do it again."

The Examiner's expression was bitter, and sad, too. Minority victims don't give a damn for statistics, he thought.

Mayb changed her approach. "Beth, we're getting our norm back. Think—really think what that means. Humans used to live in complete confidence that they would be real, hundred per cent humans, with all the senses and talents and abilities that humans can have. And we're getting that back! It's a pity, a thousand times a pity, but it has to be done like this. There is no other way!"

Her carefully chosen thoughts could not override the mental pressure which began to squeeze at them from somewhere—from the Quiet Room.

The light on the board turned yellow.

"Andi—"

"And it's a good norm," thought Mayb desperately, "chosen in a congress of the most wonderful, objective minds we have ever had on earth. Why, some of them weren't normal according to the Code they drew up! Think how brave—"

The agonizing, yammering call blared up, dwindled, flickered a moment, surged again and was suddenly gone. Through Mayb's mind trickled the phrase "in at the death." She knew it came from the Examiner, who was standing stiffly, his face registering a harrowing repulsion. He turned abruptly and threw a lever. The incinerator was fed.

"Don't cry. It's better this way," Mayb radiated to the weeping woman. "It's better for him. He never could have been happy, even if men left him alone. Poor, poor unfinished little thing—imagine the life he'd have, always able to speak, never to know when he shouted or screamed, and never being able to hear except with his ears—the only nontelepath in the whole world!"

MEDUSA

I WASN'T sore at them. I didn't know what they'd done to me, exactly—I knew that some of it wasn't so nice, and that I'd probably never be the same again. But I was a volunteer, wasn't I? I'd asked for it. I'd signed a paper authorizing the department of commerce of the league to use me as they saw fit. When they pulled me out of the fleet for routine examinations, and when they started examinations that were definitely not routine, I didn't kick. When they asked for volunteers for a project they didn't bother to mention by name, I accepted it sight unseen. And now—

"How do you feel, Rip?" old Doc Renn wanted to know. He spoke to me easylike, with his chin on the backs of his hands and his elbows on the table. The greatest name in psychoscience, and he talks to me as if he were my old man. Right up there in front of the whole psycho board, too.

"Fine, sir," I said. I looked around. I know all the doctors and one or two of the visitors. All the medicos had done one job or another on me in the last three years. Boy, did they put me through the mill. I understood only a fraction of it all—the first color tests, for instance, and the electro-coordination routines. But that torture machine of Grenfell's, and that copper helmet that Winton made me wear for two months—talk about your nightmares! What they were doing to or for me was something I could only guess at. Maybe they were testing me for something. Maybe I was just a guinea pig. Maybe I was in training for something. It was no use asking, either. I volunteered, didn't I?

"Well, Rip," Doc Renn was saying, "it's all over

98

now—the preliminaries, I mean. We're going ahead with the big job."

"Preliminaries?" I goggled. "You mean to tell me that what I've been through for the last three years was all preliminaries?"

Renn nodded, watching me carefully. "You're going on a little trip. It may not be fun, but it'll be interesting."

"Trip? Where to?" This was good news; the repeated drills on spaceship techniques, the refresher courses on astrogation, had given me a good-sized itch to get out into the black again.

"Sealed orders," said Renn, rather sharply. "You'll find out. The important thing for you to remember is that you have a very important role to play." He paused; I could see him grimly ironing the snappiness out of his tone. Why in Canaan did he have to be so careful with *me*? "You will be put aboard a Forfield Super—the latest and best equipped that the league can furnish. Your job is to tend the control machinery, and to act as assistant astrogator no matter what happens. Without doubt you will find your position difficult at times. You are to obey your orders as given, without question, and without the use of force where possible."

This sounded screwy to me. "That's all written up, just about word for word, in the 'Naval Manual,'" I reminded him gently, "under 'Duties of Crew.' I've had to do all you said every time I took a ship out. Is there anything special about this one, that it calls for all this underlining?"

He was annoyed, and the board shuffled twenty-two pairs of feet. But his tone was still friendly, half-persuasive when he spoke. "There is definitely something special about this ship, and—its crew. Rip, you've come through everything we could hand you, with flying colors. Frankly, you were subjected to psychic forces that were enough to drive a normal man quite mad. The rest of the crew—it is only fair to tell you—are insane. The nature of this expedition necessitates our manning the ship that way. Your place on the ship is a key position. Your responsibility is a great one."

"Now—hold on, sir," I said. "I'm not questioning your orders, sir, and I consider myself under your disposition. May I ask a few questions?"

He nodded.

"You say the crew is insane. Isn't that a broad way of putting it—" I couldn't help needling him; he was trying so hard to keep calm—"for a psychologist?"

He actually grinned. "It is. To be more specific, they're schizoids—dual personalities. Their primary egos are paranoiac. They're perfectly rational except on the subject of their particular phobia—or mania, as the case may be. The recessive personality is a manic depressive."

Now, as I remembered it, most paranoiacs have delusions of grandeur coupled with a persecution mania. And a manic depressive is the "Yes master" type. They just didn't mix. I took the liberty of saying as much to one of Earth's foremost psychoscientists.

"Of course they don't mix," snapped Renn. "I didn't say they did. There's no interflowing of egos in these cases. They are schizoids. The cleavage is perfect."

I have a mole under my arm that I scratch when I'm thinking hard. I scratched it. "I didn't know anything like that existed," I said. Renn seemed bent on keeping this informal, and I was playing it to the limit. I sensed that this was the last chance I'd have to get any information about the expedition.

"There never were any cases like that until recently," said Renn patiently. "Those men came out of our laboratories."

"Oh. Sort of made-to-order insanity?" He nodded.

"What on earth for, sir?"

"Sealed orders," he said immediately. His manner became abrupt again. "You take off tomorrow. You'll be put aboard tonight. Your commanding officer is Captain William Parks." I grinned delightedly at this. Parks—the horny old fireater! They used to say of him that he could create sunspots by spitting straight up. But he was a real spaceman—through and through.

"And don't forget, Rip," Renn finished. "There is only one sane man aboard that ship. That is all."

I saluted and left.

A Forfield Super is as sweet a ship as anything ever launched. There's none of your great noisy bulk pushed through the ether by a cityful of men, nor is it your completely automatic "Eyehope"—so called because after you slipped your master control tape into the automatic pilot you always said, "you're on your way, you little hunk of tinfoil—I hope!"

With an eight-man crew, a Forfield can outrun and outride anything else in space. No rockets—no celestial helices—no other such clumsy nonsense drives it. It doesn't go places by going—it gets there by standing still. By which I mean that the ship achieves what laymen call "Universal stasis."

The Galaxy is traveling in an orbit about the mythical Dead Center at an almost incredible velocity. A Forfield, with momentum nullified, just stops dead while the Galaxy streams by. When the objective approaches, momentum is resumed, and the ship appears in normal space with only a couple of thousand miles to go. That is possible because the lack of motion builds up a potential in motion; motion, being a relative thing, produces a set of relative values.

Instead of using the terms "action" and "reaction" in speaking of the Forfield drive, we speak of "stasis" and "re-stasis." I'd explain further but I left my spherical slide rule home. Let me add only that a Forfield can achieve stasis in regard to planetary, solar, galactic or universal orbits. Mix 'em in the right proportions, and you get resultants that will take you anywhere, fast.

I was so busy from the instant I hit the deck that I didn't have time to think of all the angles of this more-than-peculiar trip. I had to check and double-check every control and instrument from the milliammeter to the huge compound integrators, and with a twenty-four-hour deadline that was no small task. I also had to take a little instruction from a league master mechanic who had installed a couple of gadgets which had been designed and tested at the last minute expressly for this trip. I paid little attention to what went on round me; I didn't even know the skipper was aboard until I rose from my knees before the integrators, swiveled around on my way to the control board, and all but knocked the old war horse off his feet.

"Rip! I'll be damned!" he howled. "Don't tell me— you're not signed on here?"

"Yup," I said. "Let go my hand, skipper—I got to be able to hold a pair of needle noses for another hour or so. Yeah, I heard you were going to captain this barrel. How do you like it?"

"Smooth," he said, looking around, then bringing his grin back to me. He only grinned twice a year because it hurt his face; but when he did, he did it all over. "What do you know about the trip?"

"Nothing except that we have sealed orders."

"Well, I'll bet there's some kind of a honkatonk at the end of the road," said Parks. "You and I've been on . . . how many is it? Six? Eight . . . anyway, we've been on plenty of ships together, and we managed to throw a whingding ashore every trip. I hope we can get out Aldeberan way. I hear Susie's place is under new management again. Heh! Remember the time we—"

I laughed. "Let's save it, skipper. I've got to finish this check-up, and fast. But, man, it's good to see you again." We stood looking at each other, and then something popped into my head and I felt my smile washing off. What was it that Dr. Renn had said—"Remember there's only one sane man aboard!" Oh, no —they hadn't put Captain Parks through that! Why—

I said, "How do you—feel, cap'n?"

"Swell," he said. He frowned. "Why? You feel all right?"

Not right then, I didn't. Captain Parks batty? That was just a little bit lousy. If Renn was right—and he was always right—then his board had given Parks the works, as well as the rest of the crew. All but me, that is. I *knew* I wasn't crazy. I didn't feel crazy. "I feel fine," I said.

"Well, go ahead then," said Parks, and turned his back.

I went over to the control board, disconnected the power leads from the radioscope, and checked the dials. For maybe five minutes I felt the old boy's eyes drilling into the nape of my neck, but I was too upset to say anything more. It got very quiet in there. Small noises drifted into the control room from other parts of the ship. Finally I heard his shoulder brush the doorpost as he walked out.

How much did the captain know about this trip? Did he know that he had a bunch of graduates from the laughing academy to man his ship? I tried to picture Renn informing Parks that he was a paranoiac and a manic depressive, and I failed miserably. Parks would probably take a swing at the doctor. Aw, it just didn't make sense. It occurred to me that "making sense" was a criterion that we put too much faith in. What do you do when you run across something that isn't even supposed to make sense?

I slapped the casing back on the radioscope, connected the leads, and called it quits. The speaker over the forward post rasped out, "All hands report to control chamber!" I started, stuck my tools into their clips under the chart table and headed for the door. Then I remembered I was already in the control room, and subsided against the bulkhead.

They straggled in. All hands were in the pink, well fed and eager. I nodded to three of them, shook hands with another. The skipper came in without looking at me—I rather thought he avoided my eyes. He went straight forward, faced about and put his hands low enough on the canted control board so he could sit on them. Seabiscuit, the quartermaster, and an old shipmate of mine, came and stood beside me. There was an embarrassed murmur of voices while we all awaited the last two stragglers.

Seabiscuit whispered to me, "I once said I'd sail clear to Hell if Bill Parks was cap'n of the ship."

I said, out of the side of my face, "So?"

"So it looks like I'm goin' to," said the Biscuit.

The captain called the roll. That crew was microscopically hand picked. I had heard every single one of the names he called in connection with some famous escapade or other. Harry Voight was our chemist. He is the man who kept two hundred passengers alive for a month with little more than a week's supply of air and water to work with, after the liner crossed bows with a meteorite on the Pleione run. Bort Brecht was the engineer, a man who could do three men's work with his artificial hand alone. He lost it in the *Pretoria* disaster. The gunner was Hoch McCoy, the guy who "invented" the bow and arrow and saved his life when he was marooned on an asteroid in the middle of a pack of poison-toothed "Jackrabbits." The mechanics were Phil and Jo Hartley, twins, whose resemblance enabled them to change places time and again during the Insurrection, thus running bales of vital information to the league high command.

"Report," he said to me.

"All's well in the control chamber, sir," I said formally.

"Brecht?"

"All's well back aft, sir."

"Quartermaster?"

"Stores all aboard and stashed away, sir," said the Biscuit.

Parks turned to the control board and threw a lever. The air locks slid shut, the thirty-second departure signal began to sound from the oscillator on the hull and from signals here and in the engineer's chamber. Parks raised his voice to be heard over their clamor.

"I don't know where we're goin',", he said, with an odd smile, "but—" the signals stopped, and that was deafening—"we're on our way!"

The master control he had thrown had accomplished all the details of taking off—artificial gravity, "solar" and "planetary" stases, air pumps, humidifiers—everything. Except for the fact that there was suddenly no light streaming in through the portholes any more, there was no slightest change in sensation. Parks reached out and tore the seals off the tape slot on the integrators and from the door of the orders file. He

opened the cubbyhole and drew out a thick envelope.
There was something in my throat I couldn't swallow.

He tore it open and pulled out eight envelopes and
a few folded sheets of paper. He glanced at the envelopes and, with raised eyebrows, handed them to
me. I took them. There was one addressed to each
member of the crew. At a nod from the skipper I dis-
tributed them. Parks unfolded his orders and looked
at them.

"Orders," he read. "By authority of the Solar
League, pertaining to destination and operations of
Xantippean Expedition No. 1."

Startled glances were batted back and forth.
Xantippe! No one had ever been to Xantippe! The
weird, cometary planet of Betelgeuse was, and had
always been, taboo—and for good reason.

Parks's voice was tight. "Orders to be read to crew
by the captain immediately upon taking off." The skipper went to the pilot chair, swiveled it, and sat down.
The crew edged closer.

"The league congratulates itself on its choice of a
crew for this most important mission. Out of twenty-
seven hundred volunteers, these eight men survived
the series of tests and conditioning exercises provided
by the league.

"General orders are to proceed to Xantippe. Captain and crew have been adequately protected against
the field. Object of the expedition is to find the cause
of the Xantippe Field and to remove it.

"Specific orders for each member of the crew are
enclosed under separate sealed covers. The crew is ordered to read these instructions, to memorize them,
and to destroy the orders and envelopes. The league
desires that these orders be read in strictest secrecy by
each member of the crew, and that the individual contents of the envelopes be held as confidential until con-
trary orders are issued by the league." Parks drew a
deep breath and looked around at his crew.

They were a steady lot. There was evidence of excitement, of surprise, and in at least one case, of shock.
But there was no fear. Predominantly, there was a
kind of exultance in the spaceburned, hard-bitten

faces. They bore a common glory, a common hatred. "That isn't sensible," I told myself. "It isn't natural, or normal, or sane, for eight men to face madness, years of it, with that joyous light in their eyes. But then—they're mad already, aren't they? *Aren't they?*"

It was catching, too. I began to hate Xantippe. Which was, I suppose, silly. Xantippe was a planet, of a sort. Xantippe never killed anybody. It drove men mad, that was all. More than mad—it fused their synapses, reduced them to quivering, mindless hulks, drooling, their useless minds turned super-cargo in a useless body. Xantippe had snared ship upon ship in the old days; ships bound for the other planets of the great star. The mad planet used to blanket them in its mantle of vibrations, and they were never heard from again. It was years before the league discovered where the ships had gone, and then they sent patrols to investigate. They lost eighteen ships and thirty thousand men that way.

And then came the Forfield drive. In the kind of static hyperspace which these ships inhabited, surely they would pass the field unharmed. There were colonists out there on the other planets, depending on supplies from Sol. There were rich sources of radon, uranium, tantalum, copper. Surely a Forfield ship could—

But they couldn't. They were the first ships to penetrate the field, to come out on the other side. The ships were intact, but their crews could use their brains for absolutely nothing. Sure, I hated Xantippe. Crazy planet with its cometary orbit and its unpredictable complex ecliptic. Xantippe had an enormous plot afoot. It was stalking us—even now it was ready to pounce on us, take us all and drain our minds—

I shook myself and snapped out of it. I was dreaming myself into a case of the purple willies. If I couldn't keep my head on my shoulders aboard this spacegoing padded cell, then who would? Who else could?

The crew filed out, muttering. Parks sat on the pilot's chair, watching them, his bright gaze flitting from face to face. When they had gone he began to watch me. Not look at me. Watch me. It made me sore.

"Well?" he said after a time.

"Well *what?*" I barked, insubordinately.

"Aren't you going to read your bedtime story? I am."

"Bed—oh." I slit the envelope, unfolded my orders. The captain did likewise at the extreme opposite side of the chamber. I read:

"Orders by authority of the Solar League pertaining to course of action to be taken by Harl Ripley, astromechanic on Xantippean Expedition No. 1.

"Said Harl Ripley shall follow the rules and regulations as set forth in the naval regulations, up until such time as the ship engages the Xantippean Field. He is then to follow the orders of the master, except in case of the master's removal from active duty from some unexpected cause. Should such an emergency arise, the command does not necessarily revert to said Harl Ripley, but to the crew member who with the greatest practicability outlines a plan for the following objective: The expedition is to land on Xantippe; if uninhabited, the planet is to be searched until the source of the field is found and destroyed. If inhabited, the procedure of the pro-tem commander must be dictated by events. He is to bear in mind, however, that the primary and only purpose of the expedition is to destroy the Xantippean Field."

That ended the orders; but scrawled across the foot of the page was an almost illegible addendum: "Remember your last board meeting, Rip. And good luck!" The penciled initials were C. Renn, M. Ps. S. That would be Doc Renn.

I was so puzzled that my ears began to buzz. The government had apparently spent a huge pile of money in training us and outfitting the expedition. And yet our orders were as hazy as they could possibly be. And what was the idea of giving separate orders to each crew member? And such orders! "The procedure of the pro-tem commander must be dictated by events." That's what you'd call putting us on our own! It wasn't like the crisp, detailed commands any navy man is used to. It was crazy.

Well, of course it was crazy, come to think of it. What else could you expect with this crew? I began to wish sincerely that the board had driven me nuts along with the rest of them.

I was at the chart table, coding up the hundred-hour log entry preparatory to slipping it into the printer, when I sensed someone behind me. The skipper, of course. He stayed there a long time, and I knew he was watching me.

I sat there until I couldn't stand it any longer. "Come on in," I said without moving. Nothing happened. I listened carefully until I could hear his careful breathing. It was short, swift. He was trying to breathe in a whisper. I began to be really edgy. I had a nasty suspicion that if I whirled I would be just in time to catch a bolt from a by-by gun.

Clenching my jaw till my teeth hurt, I rose slowly, and without looking around, went to the power-output telltales and looked at them. I didn't know what was the matter with me. I'd never been this way before—always expecting attack from somewhere. I used to be a pretty nice guy. As a matter of fact, I used to be the nicest guy I knew. I didn't feel that way any more.

Moving to the telltales took me another six or eight feet from the man at the door. Safer for both of us. And this way I had to turn around to get back to the table. I did. It wasn't the skipper. It was the chemist, Harry Voight. We were old shipmates, and I knew him well.

"Hello, Harry. Why the dark-companion act?"

He was tense. He was wearing a little mustache of perspiration on his upper lip. His peculiar eyes—the irises were as black as the pupils—were set so far back in his head that I couldn't see them, for the alleyway light was directly over his head. His bald, bulging forehead threw two deep purple shadows, and out of them he watched me.

"Hi, Rip. Busy?"

"Not too busy. Put it in a chair."

He came in and sat down. He turned as he passed

me, backed into the pilot's seat. I perched on the chart table. It looked casual, and it kept my weight on one foot. If I had to move in any direction, including up, I was ready to.

After a time he said, "What do you think of this, Rip?" His gesture took in the ship, Xantippe, the league, the board.

"I only work here," I quoted. That was the motto of the navy. Our insignia is the league symbol superimposed on a flaming sun, under which is an ultraradio screen showing the words, "I only work here." The famous phrase expresses the utmost in unquestioning, devoted duty.

Harry smiled a very sickly smile. If ever I saw a man with something eating him, it was Harry Voight. "S'matter," I asked quietly. "Did somebody do you something?"

He looked furtively about him, edged closer. "Rip, I want to tell you something. Will you close the door?"

I started to refuse, and then reflected that regulations could stand a little relaxing in a coffin like this one. I went and pressed the panel, and it slid closed. "Make it snappy," I said. "If the skipper comes up here and finds that door closed he'll slap some wrists around here."

As soon as the door closed, Harry visibly slumped. "This is the first time in two days I've felt—comfortable," he said. He looked at me with sudden suspicion. "Rip—when we roomed together in Venus City, what color was that jacket I used to keep my 'Naval Manual' in?"

I frowned. I'd only seen the thing a couple of times —"Blue," I said.

"That's right." He wiped his forehead. "You're O.K." He made a couple of false starts and then said, "Rip, will you keep everything I say strictly to yourself? Nobody can be trusted here—nobody!" I nodded. "Well," he went on in a strained voice, "I know that this is a screwy trip. I know that the crew is—has been made—sort of—well, not normal—"

He said, with conviction, "The league has its own reason for sending us, and I don't question them. But something has gone wrong. You think Xantippe is going to get us? Ha! Xantippe is getting us *now*!" He sat back triumphantly.

"You don't say!"

"But I do! I know she's countless thousands of light years away. But I don't have to tell you of the power of Xantippe. For a gigantic power like that, a little project like what they're doing to us is nothing. Any force that can throw out a field three quarters of a billion miles in diameter can play hell with us at a far greater distance."

"Could be," I said. "Just what are they doing?"

"They're studying us," he hissed. "They're watching each of us, our every action, our every mental reflex. And one by one they are—taking us away! They've got the Hartley twins, and Bort Brecht, and soon they'll have me. I don't know about the others, but their turns will come. They are taking away our personalities, and substituting their own. I tell you, those three men—and soon now, I with them—those men are not humans, but Xantippeans!"

"Now wait," I said patiently. "Aren't you going on guesswork? Nobody knows if Xantippe's inhabited. And I doubt that this substitution you speak of can be done."

"You don't think so? For pity's sake, Rip—for your own good, try to believe me! The Xantippean Field is a thought force, isn't it? And listen—I know it if you don't—this crew was picked for its hatred of Xantippe. Don't you see why? The board expects that hatred to act as a mental 'fender'—to partly ward off the field. They think there might be enough left of our minds when we're inside the field to accomplish our objective. They're wrong, Rip—*wrong!* The very existence of our communal hatred is the thing that has given us away. They have been ready for us for days now—and they are already doing their work aboard."

He subsided, and I prodded him with gentle questions.

"How do you know the Xantippeans have taken away those three men?"

"Because I happened to overhear the Hartley twins

talking in the messroom two days ago. They were talking about their orders. I know I should not have listened, but I was already suspicious."

"They were talking about their orders? I understood that the orders were confidential."

"They were. But you can't expect the Hartleys to pay much attention to that. Anyway, Jo confided that a footnote on his orders had intimated that there was only one sane man aboard. Phil laughed that off. He said he knew he was sane, and he knew that Jo was sane. Now, I reason this way. Only a crazy man would question the league; a crazy man or an enemy. Now the Hartleys may be unbalanced, but they are still rational. They are still navy men. Therefore, they must be enemies, because navy men never question the league."

I listened to that vague logic spoken in that intense, convincing voice, and I didn't know what to think. "What about Bort Brecht—and yourself?"

"Bort! Ahh!" His lips curled. "I can sense an alien ego when I speak to him. It's overwhelming. I hate Xantippe," he said wildly, "but I hate Bort Brecht more! The only thing I could possibly hate more than Xantippe would be a Xantippean. That proves my point!" He spread his hands. "As for me—Rip, I'm going mad. I feel it. I see things—and when I do, I will be another of them. And then we will all be lost. For there is only one sane man aboard this ship, and that is me, and when I'm turned into an Xantippean, we will be doomed, and I want you to kill me!" He was half hysterical. I let him simmer down.

"And do I look crazy?" I asked. "If you are the only sane man—"

"Not crazy," he said quickly. "A schizoid—but you're perfectly rational. You must be, or you wouldn't have remembered what color my book jacket was."

I got up, reached out a hand to help him to his feet. He drew back. "Don't touch me!" he screamed, and when I recoiled, he tried to smile. "I'm sorry, Rip, but I can't be sure about anything. You may be a Xantippean by now, and touching me might . . . I'll be going now . . . I—" He went out, his black, burning eyes half closed.

I stood at the door watching him weave down the alleyway. I could guess what was the matter. Paranoia —but bad! There was the characteristic persecution mania, the intensity of expression, the peculiar single-track logic—even delusions of grandeur. Heh! He thought *he* was the one mentally balanced man aboard!

I walked back to the chart table, thinking hard. Harry always had been pretty tight-lipped. He probably wouldn't spread any panic aboard. But I'd better tip the captain off. I was wondering why the Hartley twins and Harry Voight had all been told that all hands but me were batty, when the skipper walked in.

"Rip," he said without preamble. "Did you ever have a fight with Hoch McCoy?"

"Good gosh, no!" I said. "I never saw him in my life until the day we sailed. I've heard of him, of course. Why?"

Parks looked at me oddly. "He just left my quarters. He had the most long-winded and detailed song and dance about how you were well known as an inter-solar master saboteur. Gave names and dates. The names I know well. But the dates—well, I can alibi you for half of 'em. I didn't tell him that. But—Lord! He almost had me convinced!"

"Another one!" I breathed. And then I told him about Harry Voight.

"I don't imagine Doc Renn thought they would begin to break so soon," said Parks when I had finished. "These boys were under laboratory conditions for three solid years, you know."

"I didn't know," I said. "I don't know a damn thing that's going on around here and I'd better learn something before I go off my kilter, too."

"Why, Ripley," he said mockingly. "You're over-wrought!" Well, I was. Parks said, "I don't know much more than you do, but that goofy story of Harry Voight's has a couple of pretty shrewd guesses in it. For instance, I think he was right in assuming that the board had done something to the minds of . . . ah . . . some of the crew as armor against the field. Few men have approached it consciously—those who have were usually scared half to death. It's well known that fear forms the easiest possible entrance for the thing feared —ask any good hypnotist. Hate is something different again. Hate is a psychological block against fear and the thing to be feared. And the kind of hate that these guys have for Xantippe and the field is something extra special. They're mad, but they're not afraid—and that's no accident. When we do hit the field, it's bound to have less effect on us than it had on the crews of poor devils who tried to attack it."

"That sounds reasonable. Er . . . skipper, about this 'one sane man' business. What do you think of that?"

"More armor," said Parks. "But armor against the man himself. Harry, for instance, was made a paranoiac, which is a very sensible kind of nut; but at the same time he was convinced that he alone was sane. If he thought his mind had been actually tampered with instead of just—tested, he'd get all upset about it and, like as not, undo half the Psy Board's work."

Some of that struck some frightening chords in my memory. "Cap'n—do you believe that there is one sane, normal man aboard?"

"I do. One." He smiled slowly. "I know what you're thinking. You'd give anything to compare your orders with mine, wouldn't you?"

"I would. But I won't do it. Confidential. I couldn't let myself do it even if you agreed, because—" I paused.

"Well?"

"Because you're an officer and I'm a gentleman."

In my bunk at last, I gave over wishing that we'd get to the field and have it over with, and tried to do some constructive thinking. I tried to remember exactly what Doc Renn had said, and when I did, I was sorry I'd made the effort. "You are sane," and "You have been subjected to psychic forces that are sufficient to drive a normal man quite mad" might easily be totally different things. I'd been cocky enough to assume that

they meant the same thing. Well, face it. Was I crazy?
I didn't feel crazy. Neither did Harry Voight. He
thought he was going crazy, but he was sure he hadn't
got there yet. And what was "crazy," anyway? It was
normal, on this ship, to hate Xantippe so much that you
felt sick and sweated cold when you thought of it. Paranoia—persecution. Did I feel persecuted? Only by the
thought of our duty toward Xantippe, and the persecution was Xantippe, not the duty. Did I have delusions
of grandeur? Of course not; and yet—hadn't I blandly
assumed that Voight had such delusions because he
thought *he* was the one sane man aboard?

What was the idea of that, anyway? Why had the
board put one sane man aboard—if it had? Perhaps
to be sure that one man reacted differently to the
others at the field, so that he could command. Perhaps
merely to make each man feel that he was sane, even
though he wasn't. My poor, tired brain gave it up and
I slept.

We had two casualties before we reached the field.
Harry Voight cut his throat in the washroom, and my
gentle old buddy, Seabiscuit, crushed in the back of
Hoch McCoy's head. "He was an Insurrectionist spy,"
he insisted mildly, time and again, while we were locking him up.

After that we kept away from each other. I don't
think I spoke ten words to anyone outside of official
business, from that day until we snapped into galactic
stasis near Betelgeuse. I was sorry about Hoch, because he was a fine lad. But my sorrow was tempered
by the memory of his visit to the captain. There had
been a pretty fine chance of his doing that to me!

In normal space once more, we maneuvered our
agile little craft into an orbit about the huge sun and
threw out our detectors. These wouldn't tell us much
when the time came, for their range wasn't much more
than the radius of the field.

The mad planet swam up onto the plates and I
stared at it as I buzzed for the skipper. Xantippe was
a strangely dull planet, even this close to her star. She
shone dead silver, like a moonlit corpse's flesh. She

was wrinkled and patched, and—perhaps it was an etheric disturbance—she seemed to pulsate slowly from pole to pole. She wasn't quite round; more nearly an ovoid, with the smaller end toward Betelgeuse! She was between two and three times the size of Luna. Gazing at her, I thought of the thousands of men of my own service who had fallen prey to her, and of the fine ships of war that had plunged into the field and disappeared. Had they crashed? Had they been tucked into some weird warp of space? Were they captives of some strange and horrible race?

Xantippe had defied every type of attack so far. She swallowed up atomic mines and torpedoes with no appreciable effect. She was apparently impervious to any rayed vibration known to man; but she was matter, and should be easy meat for an infragun—if you could get an infragun close enough. The gun's twin streams of highly charged particles, positrons on one side, mesatrons on the other, would destroy anything that happened to be where they converged. But an infragun has an effective range of less than five hundred miles. Heretofore, any ship which carried the weapon that close to Xantippe carried also a dead or mindless crew.

Captain Parks called the crew into the control room as soon as he arrived. No one spoke much; they didn't need any more information after they had glanced at the view-plate which formed the forward wall of the chamber. Bort Brecht, the swarthy engineer, wanted to know how soon we'd engage the field.

"In about two hours," said the captain glibly. I got a two-handed grip on myself to keep from yapping. He was a cold-blooded liar—we'd hit it in half an hour or less, the way I figured it. I guessed that he had his own reasons. Perhaps he thought it would be easier on the crew that way.

Parks leaned casually against the integrators and faced the crew. "Well, gentlemen," he said as if he were banqueting on Earth, "we'll soon find out what this is all about. I have instructions from the league to place certain information at your disposal.

"All hands are cautioned to obey the obvious commander once we're inside the field. That commander may or may not be myself. That has been arranged for. Each man must keep in mind the objective—the destruction of the Xantippean Field. One of us will lead the others toward that objective. Should no one seem to be in command a pro-tem captain is to be elected."

Brecht spoke up. "Cap'n, how do we know that this 'commander' that has been arranged for isn't Harry Voight or Hoch McCoy?"

"We don't know," said Parks gravely. "But we will. We will."

Twenty-three minutes after Xantippe showed up on the plates, we engaged her field.

All hands were still in the control room when we plunged in. I remember the sudden weakness of my limbs, and the way all five of the others slipped and slid down to the deck. I remember the Biscuit's quaver, "I tell you it's all a dirty Insurrectionist plot." And then I was down on the deck, too.

Something was hurting me, but I knew exactly where I was. I was under Dr. Grenfell's torture machine; it was tearing into my mind, chilling my brain. I could feel my brains, every last convolution of them. They were getting colder and colder, and bigger and bigger, and pretty soon now they would burst my skull and the laboratory and the building and chill the earth. Inside my chest I was hot, and of course I knew why. I was Betelgeuse, mightiest of suns, and with my own warmth I warmed half a galaxy. Soon I would destroy it, too, and that would be nice.

All the darkness in Great Space came to me.

Leave me alone. I don't care what you want done. I just want to lie here and— But nobody wanted me to do anything. What's all the hollering about, then? Oh. *I* wanted something done. There's something that has to be done, so get up, get up, get—

"He *is* dead. Death is but a sleep and a forgetting, and he's asleep, and he's forgotten everything, so he must be dead!" It was Phil Hartley. He was down on his hunkers beside me, shrieking at the top of his voice, mouthing and pointing like an ape completely caught up in the violence of his argument. Which was odd, because he wasn't arguing with anybody. The skipper was sitting silently in the pilot's chair, tears streaming down his cheeks. Jo Hartley was dead or passed out on the deck. The Biscuit and Bort Brecht were sitting on the deck holding hands like children, staring entranced into the viewplate. It showed a quadrant of Xantippe, filling the screen. The planet's surface did indeed pulsate, and it was a beautiful sight. I wanted to watch it drawing closer and closer, but there was something that had to be done first.

I sat up achingly. "Get me some water," I muttered to Phil Hartley. He looked at me, shrieked, and went and hid under the chart table.

The vision of Xantippe caught and held me again, but I shook it off. It was the most desirable thing I'd ever seen, and it promised me all I could ever want, but there was something I had to do first. Maybe someone could tell me. I shook the skipper's shoulder.

"Go away," he said. I shook him again. He made no response. Fury snapped into my brain. I cuffed him with my open hand, front and back, front and back. He leaped to his feet, screamed, "Leave me alone!" and slumped back into the chair. At the sound Bort Brecht lurched to his feet and came over to us. When he let go Seabiscuit's hand, the Biscuit began to cry quietly.

"I'm giving the orders around here," Bort said.

I was delighted. There had been something, a long time ago, about somebody giving orders. "I have to do something," I said. "Do you know what it is?"

"Come with me." He led the way, swaggering, to the screen. "Look," he commanded, and then sat down beside Seabiscuit and lost himself in contemplation. Seabiscuit kept on crying.

"That's not it," I said doubtfully. "I think you gave me the wrong orders."

"Wrong?" he bellowed. "Wrong? I am never wrong!" He got up, and before I knew what was coming, he hauled off and cracked three knuckles with my jawbone. I hit the deck with a crash and slid up against Jo Hartley. Jo didn't move. He was alive, but

he just didn't seem to give a damn. I lay there for a
long time before I could get up again. I wanted to kill
Bort Brecht, but there was something I had to do first.

I went back to the captain and butted him out of the
chair. He snarled at me and went and crouched by
the bulkhead, tears still streaming down his cheeks. I
slumped into the seat, my fingers wandering idly about
the controls without touching them, my eyes desperately trying to avoid the glory of Xantippe.

It seemed to me that I was very near to the thing I
was to do. My right hand touched the infragun activa-
tor switch, came away, went back to it, came away.
I boldly threw another switch; a network of crosshairs
and a bright central circle appeared on the screen.
This was it, I thought. Bort Brecht yelped like a kicked
dog when the crosshairs appeared, but did not move.
I activated the gun, and grasped the range lever in
one hand and the elevation control in the other. A
black-centered ball of flame hovered near the surface
of the planet.

This was it! I laughed exultantly and pushed the
range lever forward. The ball plunged into the dull-
silver mystery, leaving a great blank crater. I pulled
and pushed at the elevation control, knowing that my
lovely little ball was burning and tearing its inexorable
way about in the planet's vitals. I drew it out to the
surface, lashed it up and down and right and left, cut
and slashed and tore.

Bort Brecht was crouched like an anthropoid, knees
bent, knuckles on the deck, fury knotting his features,
eyes fixed on the scene of destruction. Behind me Phil
Hartley was teetering on tiptoe, little cries of pain
struggling out of his lips every time the fireball appeared. Bort spun and was beside me in one great
leap. "What's happening? Who's doing that?"

"He is," I said immediately, pointing at Jo Hartley.
I knew that this was going to be tough on Jo, but I
was doing the thing I had to do, and I knew Bort
would try to stop me. Bort leaped on the prone figure,
using teeth and nails and fists and feet; and Phil
Hartley hesitated only a minute, torn between the vision of Xantippe and something that called to him

from what seemed a long, long while ago. Then Jo
cried out in agony, and Phil, a human prototype of
my fireball, struck Bort amidships. Back and forth,
fore and aft, the bloody battle raged, while Seabiscuit
whimpered and the skipper, still sunk in his introspec-
tive trance, wept silently. And I cut and stabbed and
ripped at Xantippe.

I took care now, and cut a long slash almost from
pole to pole; and the edges opened away from the
wound as if the planet had been wrapped in a paper
sheath. Underneath it was an olive-drab color, shot
with scarlet. I cut at this incision again and again,
sinking my fireball in deeper at each slash. The weak-
ened ovoid tended to press the edges together, but
the irresistible ball sheared them away as it passed;
and when it had cut nearly all the way through, the
whole structure fell in on itself horribly. I had a sudden feeling of lightness, and then unbearable agony.
I remember stretching back and back over the chair
in the throes of some tremendous attack from inside
my body, and then I struck the deck with my head
and shoulders, and I was all by myself again in the
beautiful black.

There was a succession of lights that hurt, and
soothing smells, and the sound of arcs and the sound
of falling water. Some of them were weeks apart,
some seconds. Sometimes I was conscious and could
see people tiptoeing about. Once I thought I heard
music.

But at last I awoke quietly, very weak, to a hand
on my shoulder. I looked up. It was Dr. Renn. He
looked older.

"How do you feel, Rip?"

"Hungry."

He laughed. "That's splendid. Know where you
are?"

I shook my head, marveling that it didn't hurt
me.

"Earth," he said. "Psy hospital. You've been
through the mill, son."

"What happened?"

"Plenty. We got the whole story from the picrecording tapes inside and outside of your ship. You cut Xantippe all to pieces. You incidentally got Bort Brecht started on the Hartley family, which later literally cut *him* to pieces. It cost three lives, but Xantippe is through."

"Then—I destroyed the projector, or whatever it was—"

"You destroyed Xantippe. You—killed Xantippe. The planet was a . . . a thing that I hardly dare think about. You ever see a hydromedusa here on Earth?"

"You mean one of those jellyfish that floats on the surface of the sea and dangles paralyzing tentacles down to catch fish?"

"That's it. Like a Portuguese man-of-war. Well, that was Xantippe, with that strange mind field about her for her tentacles. A space dweller; she swept up anything that came her way, killed what was killable, digested what was digestible to her. Examination of the pictures, incidentally, shows that she was all set to hurl out a great cloud of spores. One more revolution about Betelgeuse and she'd have done it."

"How come I went under like that?" I was beginning to remember.

"You weren't as well protected as the others. You see, when we trained that crew we carefully split the personalities; paranoiac hatred to carry them through the field and an instant reversion to manic depressive under the influence of the field. But yours was the only personality we couldn't split. So you were the leader—you were delegated to do the job. All we could do to you was to implant a desire to destroy Xantippe. You did the rest. But when the psychic weight of the field was lifted from you, your mind collapsed. We had a sweet job rebuilding it, too, let me tell you!"

"Why all that business about the 'one sane man?' "

Renn grinned. "That was to keep the rest of the crew fairly sure of themselves, and to keep you from the temptation of taking over before you reached the field, knowing that the rest, including the captain, were not responsible for their actions."

"What about the others, after the field disappeared?"

"They reverted to something like normal. Not quite, though. The quartermaster tied up the rest of the crew just before they reached Earth and handed them over to us as Insurrectionist spies!

"But as for you, there's a command waiting for you if you want it."

"I want it," I said. He clapped me on the shoulder and left. Then they brought me a man-sized dinner.

BLABBERMOUTH

SHE WAS a lovely thing, and before either of us knew it my arms were around her and her deep eyes were all tangled up in mine. I held her a little too close a little too long, I guess; she squirmed away, got her balance and brushed me off like so much pretzel-juice.

"Sorry," I lied.

A winged eyebrow went up as two heavy lids went down.

"That's all right," she said in a voice like the sound of a cello whispering in the low register. "But you really ought to signal for a turn." I'd been trying to whip in front of a rotund individual who was about to climb into the taxi I wanted to get, and in doing so had almost knocked the girl off her feet. She turned away just in time to miss the practiced click of my heels as I tipped my hat. I sighed and flagged another cab. I had a lot of friends and knew a lot of glamour, and until this minute I had flattered myself on having a pretty picturesque string of 'em in my little black book. But now—well, I could only wish I had seen her somewhere before. She reminded me of someone I used to know a few years back, when I really was a bigshot. Instead of running an all-night radio program and writing feature articles on the side, I used to be a Power. I was in high-school and managed the basketball team. I cut a lot of ice and a lot of corners.

I stepped into the cab and gave the address of the restaurant where I was supposed to meet Sylvia. That was a date I'd worked hard to get, and now for some strange reason, I had little stomach for it. I stared out of the side window as the taxi drew past the girl I'd just run into. She was walking slowly, apparently looking at something beautiful two miles away and two hundred feet up, and there was an entrancing half-smile on her face. Her hair was long and black and it turned under just about where her straight back started to make her waist so slim; I'd never seen hair like that, but there was something about the strong, clean curve of her jaw and the way the inside corners of her eyes were lower than they should be—

"Stop!" I screamed to the cabby. He must have thought that I was about to have some kind of an attack. He was wrong, then. I had already had the attack but it had just now hit me. Anyway, he did a dollar and a half's worth of damage to his brake linings, took the dollar I threw at him as I dived out, and went his unprofitable way.

I ran to her, caught her elbow. "Hey! I—"

"Ah," she contraltoed. "My friend the Juggernaut."

"Amend that," I said quickly. "Your very dear friend Eddie Gretchen."

"Oh?" said her eyebrow, and she said, "And when and where did Eddie Gretchen become my very dear friend?"

"Damfino," I said, and we began walking. By glancing at me without turning her head, she conveyed the general idea that we were walking the same way but not together. "That's for you to figure out," I went on, "and in all sincerity I wish you would. I know you. I used to circulate around you like a bloodstream. But I honestly can't remember when it happened. You're a dream that got broken up by an alarm clock. Come on now—you have my face and you have my name. What do they mean to you?"

"I was never married to you," she said distantly. "So I haven't your name. And I don't want your face."

"With a face like yours," I said, "I can't blame—"

She actually smiled at me. "You haven't changed a bit, Eddie."

I glowed for a second and then realized that she didn't intend to help any. "All right—when was it?"

"The year Covina High beat your Filthy Five 48 to 17."

"It was 48 to 19," I said furiously, "And they were the Fighting Five."

"They were filthy," she said, and laughed richly.

"Fighting," I growled. "And besides, the referees— hey! You're not Underhanded Mazie?"

"I am not! No one knows me well enough to call me that! I'm Maria Undergaard—*Miss* Undergaard to you, Mr. Gretchen."

"Aha! Er—Mazie, m'love, what was it they called the team?"

"The Fighting Five," she acknowledged.

"Okay, Maria." I took her arm happily.

"But they were filthy," she muttered. I let it go at that.

We found a table off the avenue on which to hook our elbows and gab. I don't think I took my eyes from her once in three hours. It was unbelievable. When I had first met her, she'd been a refugee from one of the low countries, in this country about four years. She had, then, an utterly charming clipped accent, which was now replaced by beautifully schooled diction—the pluperfect English achieved only by those who have thoroughly learned it as a strange language. Ah, she'd been a killer-diller in her school days. She'd always had an odd seriousness about her, a deep and unwavering intensity; and my strongest memory of her was the sleepless night I spent after our first—and only—date. It was all wonderment. I wondered what a girl like that would ever develop into. I wondered how in blue hell she had kept me at a respectable distance all evening without using her hands. And most of all I wondered at the overwhelming sense of satisfaction I had got out of it. I never spoiled that satisfaction by asking for another date—it was too complete. For the kind of wild Indian I used to be, that was quite something. And now here she was, telling me how she had inherited a little money after she graduated, had spent four years at a small college up on the Lakes, and had been studying herself myopic ever since.

"Studying what?"

She looked at me oddly. "Spiritism. Psychic manifestations. Possession, more than anything else. I've read a million books and barked up a million wrong trees, but I—think I proved what I thought all along."

"What?"

"That possession is an established fact. That anyone can be possessed. That I myself can be possessed."

"I'd like to be sure of that," I said. She took it the nice way, though her eyes told me that she hadn't missed anything. "Psychic possession is a very strange thing. But it is not strange in the way you might think. I'm sure you've read stories—books, articles—about it. How spirits drift about in and among us, how, as elementals and familiars, they sometimes take possession, causing us to do things completely alien to ourselves. Well, it isn't like that at all. It isn't psychic—it's psychological. I have proof of that." As she spoke her eyes began to wander and her voice to fade and come in strong with her wavering gaze. She seemed to be struggling desperately to keep her attention on what she was saying; but it seemed as if she were being distracted by some conversation inaudible to me. "Did you know that a vibrating string never gives off the fullest tone unless it has a sounding board back of it? The 'spirit' that possesses people is like that. My vibrating string in the analogy is the source of that spirit—a mind emanating suspicion. The sounding board is—" She broke off, looking over her shoulder at the woman who sat alone at the next table. I'd noticed her before, because of the remarkable viciousness of her expression, and the brittle politeness of the man who had sat there with her. They seemed to be a little bit married and finding it quite a strain. Maria half rose, glanced at me, and with an effort sat down again.

"What's the matter—don't you feel well?" I asked.

"Oh no—no, I'm perfectly all—I was just . . ." She

sipped at her drink, glanced over her shoulder again, took a deep breath, smiled at me.

"Someone you know?" I queried.

She shook her head. "Where was I?"

"You were here with me, looking very lovely, and you had just told me that the possessing spirit is in reality an emanation of suspicion."

"Oh. Well, it has its sounding board in a mind which bears a guilty conscience. Suspicion and guilt; when the two of them combine, they form a very powerful psychological entity, which is actually the thing which possesses a mind opened to it."

"Sounds very involved and not overly important to me," I said, scratching my ear. "Now that you've got it, what's it get you?"

She shrugged. "What good is any knowledge, once achieved? Maybe some day someone cleverer than I will find out how to use what I have learned. As far as I'm concerned, I've learned all I—care to about it." She looked at me; there was something behind that statement and the poignant glance that went with it. She was smooth, svelte; the most equable and poised human being I had ever seen; and yet under that knee-action armor she wore was a pleading, little-girl kind of terror at something she couldn't understand. It didn't fit. It didn't make sense. It made me frightened, too, a little, and hugely anxious to share it with her, whatever it was. No matter *what* it was!

She giggled suddenly. I said, "Huh?"

"I just thought of something, Eddie. You were in an awful rush when you swept me off my feet on the Avenue. Whatever became of that appointment you had to keep?"

"Oh, that. Well, I—*holy smoke!*"

I leaped up, a horrible picture of Sylvia sitting in a restaurant for three hours, waiting for me, wafted through my mind. I excused myself to Maria's laughing face and hightailed for a phone. Halfway there it occurred to me that Maria had come out with her little reminder with peculiar suddenness. One phone booth was occupied, I noticed, by the frozen-faced gentleman lately from the table next to ours. He was ogling into the phone with a real genuine sugar-candy ogle. I hate guys like that. I slid into the next booth, dialed. While I was waiting for my connection I glanced back at my table. Maria wasn't there. I froze. This was dandy. Call up one babe to fix a stand-up while another was doing precisely the same thing to me.

I got helloed at through the receiver and asked to have Sylvia paged. Sitting back to wait, I looked out again. I'd been wrong. Maria hadn't gone. She was over at the next table, talking earnestly to the basilisk who sat there. I felt my eyebrows go up. What did she mean by lying to me about not knowing those people? And why lie about it?

I could see even at that distance how the woman's face was lowering and setting as Maria spoke swiftly in her ear. When her countenance had achieved the general lines of the bulbous bow on a battleship, she got up and started over toward the phones. I had an impulse to pop into the next booth and warn the man in there that she was coming, but I didn't want to miss my call. Just as she reached the booths and plastered her ear against the glass, I heard Sylvia's voice in my receiver.

"Hello?"

"Sylvia? This is Eddie Gretchen."

"Ah. Eddie Gretchen. I wish I didn't know you well enough to remember your name. Where have you been? Where are you?"

"It was this way," I said gently. "An old friend of mine is in trouble. I just had to lend a hand—couldn't help myself." That's true enough, I thought, and anyway, she's not listening to me.

"Too bad," she said bitterly. "Meanwhile I've waited for two and a half hours in a restaurant where I'm not known, in which I have eaten a substantial lunch and from which I have secured a pack of expensive cigarettes, and to which I have brought no money. I am to assume that you will not be here?"

"Oh, Sylvia, I can't possibly. About the check, put the manager on. He knows me. I can fix that. And Sylvia—I'm terribly sorry. I—" but she had put down the receiver. In a moment the manager's voice came over. I explained the situation, got his okay, and asked for Sylvia.

"I'm sorry," said the manager. "The lady seemed—well, miffed. Definitely miffed. She said to tell you not to hold your finger down your throat until you hear from her again, because you'll sure digest it off. Heh heh."

"Heh heh," I mimicked, and hung up. I stepped out of the booth into the messiest piece of publicized domesticity I had ever seen. It was the woman Maria had spoken to. She was just in the act of bursting into the next booth. Piling in practically on top of the hapless man inside, she gave vent to her emotions in a screaming falsetto.

"You moth-eaten old billygoat! How dare you leave me sitting alone in a fourth-rate dive while you call up that sleazy little tramp? Take your hand away from the mouthpiece, you crumb. Let her hear me. Here—get away. (Into the phone.) Listen, you home-wrecker. If you want my filthy husband you can have him. But you just better think it over. If you want his money, he hasn't any. I haven't had a new dress in six months, although I'll bet you have, you—ah, she hung up." She banged the receiver violently onto its hook and turned to her palsied spouse. "Things have come to a pretty pass," she shrieked, "when total strangers can walk up to me and tell me about your goings-on! You—"

Along about then she began to repeat herself, and my interest dwindled. I pushed my way through the crowd that had collected, and went back to Maria. She sat with her head bowed, and I really don't think she knew I had returned until I was seated and spoke to her.

"Maria—"

"Oh, Eddie—" with a bright, phony smile, "did you get it fixed up all right?"

"Yeh." I sat looking at her somberly. "You did, too."

"What?" all innocence.

"Fixed something up all right. I hate to pry, Mazie,

but you just caused a hell of a stink over there. What was the idea of tipping that woman off that her husband was daddying some sugar over the phone? How did you know what he was up to in the first place? And why the devil did you tell me you didn't know those people?"

She was a little panicked. Her eyes went wide, and she reached over and clutched my wrist. She didn't know it, but her touch on my arm clinched any argument, forever and ever. As long as she held me that way, looked at me that way, she was right; I was wrong. "Please don't be angry, Eddie. I hoped you hadn't noticed. No, I didn't lie to you. I never saw them before. How did I know what was going on? I just—knew, Eddie. Please believe me—please don't catechize me! Will you forget it—just this once? I'll try not to let it happen again! Truly I will, Eddie!"

I tried to grin those bright tear-stars out of her eyes. I put one fist under her chin, punched it gently, shaking my head. "Sure, Maria. Sure. Heck—it was nothing. Skip it."

Why I hadn't sense enough to tie the incident up with her theory of possession, I'll never know.

The fourth time I saw her I proposed. That was three hours after the third time, which was one day after the second time, which was five solid weeks after the first time. Yes, it took five weeks for me to persuade her to entrust herself to me for an evening after that occasion in the little bar off the Avenue. Twice she almost cried over the phone, and after that she laughed it off; and when she had run out of reasons for not seeing me she broke down and confessed that it was because she was afraid she would embarrass me the same way again. I had to tell her that in the first place I hadn't been embarrassed and in the second place I didn't give a damn about its happening again; I just wanted to see her. It wasn't until I threatened to walk out of a window at the studio that she finally made that second date. Eighty-seven floors is a long way, and I meant what I said.

She always insisted on going to places where we'd be more or less alone, whether it was in a hansom cab in Central Park or a walk over the Brooklyn Bridge. That suited me so well I didn't bother to wonder about it. But she'd go to any lengths to avoid being with me and strangers at the same time. So it was there in the park, at four o'clock in the afternoon on the day I'd rolled out of bed early to take her to lunch, that I proposed. It was easy. I just held both her hands and felt afraid to look into her eyes when I said,

"Hey. We got to get married."

And she smiled her very own smile and nodded. I kissed her. When a passing cop grinningly broke it up, she straightened her hat, patted the back of my hand and shook her head. "I wouldn't marry you, Eddie," she said quietly. My blood turned to salt water and began to ooze coldly out of my pores. I didn't have to ask her to say it again because she did. Then she stood up. "Let's get out of here, Eddie." One of my arms went up and yanked her back down on the bench. I stared woodenly at some kids who were feeding the ducks down on the lake.

"For a minute I was scared," I said. My voice hurt me. "I thought you said you wouldn't marry me."

"I did, Eddie."

"Yeah." I turned to her and when she saw my face she lifted her hands a little and shrank back. "Why?" I asked. "Single, aren't you?"

She nodded. "It's something that—Eddie, will you take my word for it—just this once?"

"No," I said, "I already took your word for something 'just this once.' Spill it."

"It's—about the things I studied. I spent a month or so by myself up in the mountains not long ago— did I tell you? I didn't see a soul for forty-two days. I was always susceptible to what has been called the psychic. Up there, I studied, and I tried out a lot of things, and experimented a lot. That was when I got on the right track. About possession, I mean. I found out how to open my mind to possession. I went too far. I held it open too long. It—grew that way. I can't close it. I'm a permanent susceptible, Eddie. When I came down from the mountains I was different. I always will be."

"What the hell's this all about?" I snarled. "Do you love me?"

"You don't have to ask me that," she whispered. I looked at her. I didn't have to ask her. I put my arms around her and said, with my teeth on the lobe of her ear, "Tell the rest of that nonsense to your husband on your honeymoon."

The cop came along again. I thumbed at the lake over my shoulder and told him to go jump in it. He went away laughing.

Different she might have been but her only difference was in being better, finer, sweeter than any other woman on earth. That's what I believed after our honeymoon. I believe it now, with an amendment. Then, I thought that what I just said covered everything. Since, I learned a little more. Maria did have a profound difference from other women.

It didn't show up until we came back to the city and I got back on the air again. I had a nice stretch, and she adjusted herself to it gracefully. I m. c.'d an all-night radio program from two to seven in the morning, which meant getting up around four and breakfasting at suppertime. Great stuff. That way you're fresh and ready to go in the evening when everyone else who has to work for a living is tired out from a day's work. Before I got married I had a thousand friends and a thousand places to go every night. Afterward, I couldn't see why Maria shouldn't go to at least five hundred of them with me. She didn't like the idea. Acted afraid of it. I kidded her and swore at her and annoyed her and persuaded her. "A guy like me has to have friends," I said. "Look. My program has sponsors. As long as people wire in requests for phonograph records, the sponsors know that if they're hearing the music they can't very well avoid the plugs. They renew their contracts and that's what gives me nickels and dimes to buy you ice-cream cones and automobiles and stuff. You'd be surprised how many people wire in from bars and restaurants, whether they know me personally or not, just because they saw me there during the evening. I got to get around. I can notice the slack-off already, when I've only been off the stem for a couple of weeks. Last night I played fifty-eight minutes of records and transcriptions without getting a single wire. That isn't good, babe."

And she kept saying, "Then go, Eddie. I'll be all right. I won't run away from you if you leave me alone for a few hours. Go see your friends." So I did. But it didn't work out. Those weren't stag parties I was going to. The babes all knew I was married, and when they saw me by myself all the time they got the wrong idea. A little bit of this, and I went home one night and laid down the law.

She didn't like it, but she didn't argue. She took an unconscionably long time to put on her face, but she came without a peep. I didn't expect that meekness. I told her so. She smiled without enthusiasm.

"I've asked you not to force me to come with you," she said sadly. "I guess you've just got to find out for yourself."

We started on West Fifty-second street and did it up pretty well. The evening netted us four dinner invitations, three pairs of tickets to shows on the stem, and a total of ninety-two telegrams on that night's program. Maria did me proud. There wasn't a lovelier or more charming woman under lights that night, and after the first half hour or so she seemed to be enjoying it. When I tossed her into a cab in front of the studio at one-thirty, she grinned and squeezed my hand. "Maybe I was wrong, Eddie. I hope so anyway. But it was swell."

I went on up to the studio, feeling all warm inside, and it wasn't the highballs either. Jakie Feltner was winding up the "Hits at Home" stretch, two hours of records of bands playing currently in New York spots, with a background of transcribed night-club chatter to make the unwary listener think he was listening to the real thing. He gave me a peculiar look through the plate-glass as I went in, waved his hand toward my table. I threaded my way through the record-stacks and picked up the sheaf of early wires that fed out of the teletype by my microphone. As a favor to me, Jakie used to read off the one-thirty to two wires and stack up the first few releases for me while his own were being played. I gathered that he had come across a wire of particular moment. He had. Among the run-of-the-mill requests was this little gem, marked "Personal":

HEY EDDIE BETTER KEEP THAT SHEMALE SHERLOCK YOU MARRIED OUT OF POWDER ROOMS OR SHE'LL WIND UP MINUS AN EYE. SHE WENT OVER FIVE WOMEN IN THERE ONE AFTER ANOTHER, TOLD EACH ONE EXACTLY WHAT SHE WANTED TO KNOW. TOLD MY WIFE ABOUT THE RAISE I GOT TWO MONTHS AGO. I GOT TROUBLE SON. YOU LEAVE HER HOME NEXT TIME.
                    DUKE FROM DUBUQUE.

I read it over three times. The Duke was one of my steadies, who apparently went on a telegram binge every payday. I've seen him send twenty-eight in two hours. I never did find out who he was, though he apparently saw me very often.

"Pretty, huh?" said Jakie, closing the soundproof door into the other section and coming over to me.

"Yeah," I said. "The guy's nuts." He looked over my shoulder at the Duke's wire. "Oh—that one. Could be. Maybe all these are nuts too." He riffled through the pile, tossed out three more wires.

DEAR EDDIE THERE CAME THE BRIDE AND THERE WENT THE DETAILS OF MY MONKEY-BUSINESS TO THE WAITING EARS OF THE WORLD. IF YOU CAN'T AFFORD A MUZZLE I'LL SEND YOU ONE. PLEASE PLAY "I'LL BE GLAD WHEN YOU'RE DEAD" AND DEDICATE IT TO YOUR WIFE.

                    A FRIEND.

HI EDDIE SAW THE NEW MATA HARI OF FIFTY-SECOND STREET AND WAS TOLD SHE BELONGS TO YOU. WHO'D OF THOUGHT YOU'D WED A PUBLICITY ENEMY? PLEASE PLAY "WHISPERING GRASS."

                    ANN ONYMUS.

EDDIE: DIDN'T HAVE A CHANCE TO TELL YOU AT THE TIME BUT I WISH YOU'D KEEP WHAT I TELL YOU UNDER YOUR HAT. YOUR WIFE TOLD BERGEN ABOUT MY MERGER WITH WILLIAMSON WHICH WAS DUE TOMORROW. THAT WILL COST ME ABOUT EIGHT THOUSAND. GUESS IT WASN'T MARIA'S FAULT BUT YOU SHOULD HAVE TOLD HER TO KEEP QUIET ABOUT IT.

HARRY ELLIOTT.

They were all lousy but the last one hurt the most. Harry had been a friend of mine for years. Maria and I had joined his crowd a couple of hours ago at Dave's place. Bergen and his wife were there. Bergen was Harry's A-number-one rival and competitor in the printing business. I'd known for quite some time that Harry had a deal coming up with the Williamson concern that would give him weight enough to drive Bergen underground. I gathered that now that the info had leaked out through Maria, Bergen had managed to bear down on Williamson and kill the merger. That was bad enough in itself; but imagine how I felt when I remembered that *I had positively not told Maria one word about Harry Elliott's affairs!*

Jakie said quietly, "Sorry, Eddie."

I looked at him. I felt my jaw flapping foolishly and waved him away. "Go back to your turntables, Jakie. You're on the air—remember?"

"Yeh." He went to the door, turned to give me a long look, and then dashed for the mike as his number played itself out. Jakie was swell. He'd do anything for me, I knew, but there was nothing he could do about this.

How could Maria have done these things? If she had *why* did she? I could easily see how. Anyone who goes clubbing with me has to spend a lot of time by himself, because I know so damn many people. I'm always hopping from one table to another. While I was making the rounds, I guess Maria had been getting in her work.

"That—stinks," I said.

Long practice had taught me how to maintain a free-and-easy mike style no matter how I felt, no matter how much good luck or bad had piled into me before the show. Jakie put my theme on the table and the red light in front of me flashed on. I sat back mulling over the whole dirty business and when the last chorus of my theme faded, I grabbed the mike around the neck and went to work.

"Top o' the wee sma' to ye, boys and gals. This is the man behind the mike who makes all that talking noise between the music—Eddie Gretchen's the name. We're open for business till the sun comes up and stops us, and if there's any ol' thing you want to hear over the air, drop me a wire and tell me about it. Don't call me up because I haven't the intelligence to use a phone. Before I play you some transcriptions and stuff there's a little something on my mind, viz. and to wit: There's no law yet in this country against sending me personal wires while I'm working. It's fun for you and fun for me. But there's nothing funny about hitting below the belt. I just got a sheaf of that kind of thing and I don't feel so happy about it, boys and gals. I'm not saying to quit sending them, though. Oh no. But when you do, sign your names and addresses. If I find out that the information is phony, I might like to drop around and personally cave in some faces. Think it over while Tony Reddik's swell little band shows you and you how drums are really kicked around in 'Suitcase Shuffle.' " I spun the platter and let it go.

Well, it brought results. During the show I got fourteen more wires of that sort. I think all of that powder room crowd were represented. Some of them were funny and some of them were nasty and some were just hurt about it. I got my names and addresses too. Nine of them were women. It certainly seemed as if Maria had done the most vicious piece of blabbing I'd ever heard of. She told husbands about their wives and wives about their best friends. She broke up business deals and caused fistfights and broke up more than one otherwise happy couple. I couldn't understand where she got all her information, or what on earth possessed her to spill it around. Possessed—possessed . . . the word did something to my brain. That was the thing she was always trying to tell me about. The reason she didn't want to mix with a crowd. I'd seen loose-tongued women before, but this particular woman—damn it! She was so restrained! Her every thought and movement was so perfectly controlled! Well, I thought sourly, she's going to have her chance to explain it all tonight. Every dirty lousy little bit of it.

She was asleep when I came in. I stood over her, wanting to kiss her, wanting to punch her lovely mouth, wanting to kick her teeth in, wanting to have her put her arms around me so I could cry on her shoulder. She must have sensed me near her. She put up her arms and smiled without opening her eyes. I took the telegrams out of my breast pocket and closed her fingers on them. Without a word I went into the bathroom and shut the door. As I peeled off my clothes and got into pajamas and a robe I heard her start to cry, and then be quiet again. When I went back she was lying with her face buried in the crumpled telegrams.

"I see you beat me to it," I said evenly. She turned her head ever so slightly, so that one dark eye regarded me piteously. "What do you mean?"

"Why, I was going to rub your nose in those wires myself."

She rolled over and sat up. Her face was scared and defiant, and not terribly apologetic. I hadn't expected any of that except the fear. "Don't say I didn't warn you," she said softly. "Don't say I didn't try and try to keep you from taking me to those places. Don't say I didn't try to tell you about it even before we were married."

"My mistake for shutting you up. Go on—you have the floor."

"What do you expect me to say? I'm sorry?"

"Babe, that doesn't begin to cover it." I went over to her. My gums hurt, the way my jaw was clenched, driving the teeth into them. "I want the whole story. I want to know why you are such a lousy little blabbermouth, and how you got the dirt you threw around all night."

"Sit down," she said coolly, "or you'll get a seizure and fall down."

Her eyes were very wide, and that dark something in them that had chilled me on the day we met was there. I crossed the room and sat. She began to talk in a low voice.

"I was possessed last night, Eddie. Not once, but time and time again. Oh, you're so stupid sometimes! I knew this was going to happen—I knew it, but you had to be so bull-headed and—oh, I can't blame it on you, except for not trying to understand. I'll try once more. You can take it or leave it, Eddie. I've known this was coming; I know just what to say. Funny, isn't it?

"Remember what I told you about the entity that is conceived of suspicion and born of guilt? It's a wicked little *poltergeist*—an almost solid embodiment of hate. And I'm a susceptible. Eddie, I can't be in the same room with any two people who bear suspicion and the corresponding sense of guilt! And the world is full of those people—you can't avoid them. Everyone has dozens upon dozens of petty hates and prejudices. Let me give you an example. Suppose you have a racial hatred of, say, Tibetans. You and I are sitting here, and a Tibetan walks in. Now, you know him. He has a very fine mind, or he has done you a favor, or he is a friend of a good friend of yours. You talk for a half hour, politely, and everything's all right. In your heart, though, you're saying. 'I hate your yellow hide, you sniveling filth.' Everything will still be all right as long as he is unconscious of it. But once let this thought flicker into his mind—'He dislikes me because of my race'—and then and there the *poltergeist* is born. The room is full of it, charged with it. It has body and power of its own, completely independent of you or the Tibetan. I am a susceptible. The entity approaches me. I try to avoid it. I make bright remarks. I move around the room, busy myself with some flowers, a book, anything, but it's no use. I can't escape it. I can't fight it away or close my ego to it. Suddenly it has me, completely. I am part of it. It directs me, drives me. Its whole purpose is one hate. It wants to drag your dislike and his suspicion into the light. I am its instrument now. My control is only strong enough to temper the words that burn at my lips. So instead of screaming out 'He hates you, because he hates all of your yellow kind!' I move closer to the man. I stop near him, and say out of the corner of my mouth, 'You'd better go soon. He doesn't like Tibetans and I don't know how long he can keep on being polite.' Once it's said, the *poltergeist* is nullified. The hatred between you is open, no longer secret, and secret hate is the very essence of a *poltergeist*. It dissipates, and I am free; but the damage is done. The most that I can do is to apologize, make a joke of it, say I was trying to be funny. I won't be believed, because my statement, rotten as it was, was true in its very essence and can't be denied. But if I should be believed in my apology, then the seeds of hatred and suspicion are left, and the entity is conceived all over again, and possession takes place once more, then and there. To be spared that, I never deny what I have said, and never apologize for it. It would only make it worse.

"That's how it happens, Eddie, and it can't be changed. I was always susceptible, and I made the condition permanent and acute by my experiments when I was alone in the mountains. I can't change, Eddie. I shouldn't have married you, shouldn't have done this to you. I—guess this is the wind-up. I'll get out." She tried a weak little laugh. "Good thing we haven't been married long enough to have collected a house and a mess of furniture, eh?"

"Yeh," I said. I watched her as she got up, slipped into a house coat, and began to pack. She moved swiftly about the place, collecting the little odds and ends that I had just been learning to expect in my apartment. It had taken some learning, too. Bachelor digs sure get made over when a woman comes into them. After a while I went over and got into the bed. It was still a little warm and smelled nice. I turned my face to the wall, and in a minute I heard her thump a suitcase down beside the others in the middle of the room. She was looking at me; I could feel her eyes on the nape of my neck. I knew she was dressed for the street, all ready to go.

"Maria . . ."

"Yes, Eddie?" She answered a little too quickly to hide the fact that she wasn't as collected as she hoped.

"Wake me up around four, will you? We'll eat us some scrambled eggs and then take that spin around the park like we did when we were single."

There was a thump when she dropped her handbag, and then she was all over me. I put my arms around her and held her until she gasped for breath, and then I grinned at her and got me some sleep.

After that I did my clubbing solo and let Maria build me a home. She loved it. If she missed not seeing people, she didn't complain. I guess she got used to it after a while; I know I did. Things went along beautifully until Ivor Jones, the station manager, called Jakie Feltner and me into his office one evening. Neither of us knew what was up, but we both had guesses.

Jones pursed his lips and took off his glasses as we came in. He was a dried-up little man, a stickler for detail but a pretty good man to work for. He told us to sit, handed cigarettes around.

"Boys, I want you to help me. I don't have to tell you how the station is making out. I think we all are satisfied with it, but you know and I know that a small independent broadcasting station can't make as much or pay as much as a big network outlet. Now, one of the network stations here is shutting down. It needs complete new equipment, and the corporation wouldn't mind doing it. But since there are too many stations here already, and since we are equipped up to the hilt with all the latest, I rather think they'd like to take us over. They'd boost our power ten thousand watts. We'd run all their releases and therefore share in their income. You boys, as staff announcers, stand to get a twenty-per-cent raise. How's it sound?"

"Swell," said Jakie. I nodded.

"I'm sold on it," said Jones. "If we could get Shanaman, the general manager of the Eastern Network, to feel the same way, we could come to terms. I've done all I could think of in a business way. But it'll take a little more than that. If I can mellow the old boy down a bit with a swell dinner-party, I might get him to sign the papers then and there. I want you two to come and bring your women. It'll be next Friday night. Shanaman's bringing his wife. My house. You'll be there?"

"Formal?" asked Jakie. Jones nodded.

"I'd rather not, Mr. Jones," I said. "I sort of had an engagement—"

"Break it," Jones said. "Shanaman's interested in meeting you. As a matter of fact, your show is a high spot, a real selling point for the station. You've got to come. And bring that new wife of yours. I want to meet her."

Jakie laughed and got up, slapping me on the back. "I'll persuade him, Mr. Jones. We'll be there, don't worry." He was a big fellow, that Feltner. He had me rushed out of there before I knew what went on. Cornering me in the corridor, he said, "Come on Eddie—be a sport. Don't queer that party. It means a lot to me. Claire has been acting a little peculiar lately and that party ought to fix the trouble. No kidding, Eddie—you've got to do it."

"I'll see what Maria says," I muttered, and headed for home.

Maria said she didn't like the idea. We had a long argument about it. I pointed out that it was formal, that it was a business affair, that the eight people who were there knew each other very little and had nothing but the broadest interests in common, and that anyway I couldn't avoid it. It was orders. I also mentioned the fact that Jakie wanted me to do it, and I was a good friend of his. Maria's arguments were all old stuff to me, but for one new one. She was afraid that she wouldn't be able to stand it. When she had been in more or less constant contact with people, she was conditioned to the influx of possessions. Now, it was different. She feared it. It was months since she had been through it; she was afraid of what it might do to her. But I had my way, and Friday night found us walking into Jones's place in Queens Village.

It was quite a layout. Jones had a nice income and used it. Big house, big rooms, big butler. We were the last to arrive. We got rid of our coats and were shown into the library, where cocktails were being served. I stopped at the door and looked around the room. Over in a corner Jones was talking to a stout old apple who seemed all jowls and boiled shirt. Shanaman, I surmised. Talking uninterestedly with Jones's slightly washed-out wife, was Claire Feltner. I knew her well; she hung around the studio a lot. A nasty thought occurred to me; I noticed Claire there many a time when Jakie was out. Jones always seemed to be around at the time. I began to see why Jakie had been so anxious to bring Claire and Jones into the same room. He wanted to watch them. That was bad.

I rescued Jakie from the voluminous feminine counterpart of Shanaman. The network manager's wife had poor Feltner in a corner and was pounding his ear frighteningly with an account of her husband's metabolism.

Introductions were made all around, and I left Maria with Jakie while I joined Jones and Shanaman. The talk was general and too loud. Just about then I began to wish I hadn't come. That went on all the time I was there. I disliked particularly this business of our being in that big room free to wander from person to person for Lord knows how long until dinner was served. In a matter of minutes Maria could stumble across one of her little *poltergeists,* and then—well, in a matter of minutes Maria did.

Shanaman was building up to a terrific climax in an unfunny story, when I saw Maria across the room from me, looking from Shanaman to Mrs. Jones and back again. There was something about her stance, her eyes, that told me she was fighting the thing. I broke away from Shanaman as fast as I could. Not fast enough. Maria got to Mrs. Jones before I did, sat down beside her, began talking swiftly. As I got there, Mrs. Jones rose, glaring at Shanaman, and went over to her husband.

"What goes on?" I asked anxiously.

"Oh, Eddie, it happened again." She would have cried if I hadn't caught her hands, squeezed them until they hurt. "Shanaman plans to put a network crew in your station if he takes it over. Everyone will lose his job, except you, Eddie!"

"And you told that to Mrs. Jones?"

"Yes—don't you see? She suspected it, and Shanaman knew he was going to do it! I couldn't help myself, Eddie!"

"That's all right, kid," I whispered. "No hair off our necks." I watched the Joneses. It seemed to me that he didn't believe his wife. She was evidently furious with him for his stupidity and said so into his ear. He turned his back on her and went to Claire Feltner. She went over to see if she couldn't pump some information out of Shanaman. Jakie stood near them, glumly watching his wife puckering up to Jones.

"Try to keep away from Jakie," I said, turning back to Maria. But she had slipped away when I was looking at Jones. She was standing by the window behind me, kneading her hands and staring out into the night. I figured it was best to leave her alone as long as she could stand it. Meanwhile, I was going to try to keep the rest of them away from her. I barged in on Shanaman's conversation with Mrs. Jones. It was short and sweet. She was just winding up what must have been quite a scintillating piece of vituperation.

"—and don't think I don't know what you're up to, you old wolf," she was saying. She was hopping mad. Shanaman looked bewilderedly indignant. It was too late to do anything about it.

"My dear lady," he said pompously, "I regret exceedingly that your suspicions should have reached such a state. Ah—Mr. Jones. Will you come here a minute?" Jones looked up, saw what was happening, came rabbiting over. I saw the studio deal flitting out the window when I saw Jones reach out and clip his wife across the mouth. Shanaman held up his hands in horror, then barged across the room to his wife.

Then everything happened at once. Maria popped up from nowhere, nudged Jakie Feltner, whispered in his ear, nodded toward Claire. Jakie roared, reached out, spun Jones around and smeared him with a terrific right hook. Shanaman, fear of publicity plastered all over his fat face, bolted for the door with his wife.

And that was the wind-up of Jones's precious little dinner party. Maria filled in the details for me on the way home. It seemed that Jones had been seeing Jakie's wife, and Maria, possessed, told Jakie how far it had gone, and he punched Jones's mouth. Mrs. Jones's hysterical calling of Shanaman's bluff sprang, I imagine, from jealousy and the desire to hurt Jones. It was an unholy mess, one of those awful things that are awful when they happen and funny afterward. Except for one thing. Jones didn't get up after Jakie knocked him down. He smashed his silly brains out on the brass andiron in the fireplace.

The rest of it was rough. When the trial was over and poor old Feltner got sent up for thirty years on a second-degree murder charge, there wasn't much left for me. Unfavorable publicity pulled a lot of advertising contracts, and anyway, as I said, there are too many radio stations in this town. But the notoriety hadn't finished with me when it took my living away from me. Eddie Gretchen turned out to be the guy with a thousand friends who never heard of him. The radio game was strictly on the receiving end, for me. Old Shanaman's bolting for the door the night of the murder hadn't done him a bit of good; he was subpoenaed and put on the grill with the rest of us. I hadn't liked the way he cried about it—after all, big shots and little, we were all in the same boat—and he got even with me by passing the word around the studios that I wasn't to get so much as an audition.

That, after seven years in radio! Yeah, it was rough. I'd always had money and I didn't know how to go about being poor. I learned. Maria had a couple of grand in the cooler but that went quickly, along with what I'd saved, which wasn't a hell of a lot. I hit the jolly old rock-ribbed bottom the day I tried to get a job as a studio page and got well treated until somebody remembered me and I got handed the rush. The smell even reached into publishing houses, and the feature articles I used to sell brought checks every six months instead of every two weeks. I sold a little stuff under a phony name; but for that Maria and I would have starved. We lost our place and our furniture and the car. Bad. But I couldn't lose Maria. She almost left me right after the trial, feeling herself guilty of Jones's murder. I talked her out of that, telling her that he had it coming to him anyway; and then she got morbid and turned on the gas one day. I got there in time, and the police emergency squad brought her around. After that she buckled down like the ace she was, and tried helping instead of hindering. God, when I think of her down on her four bones scrubbing floors, and rubbing her white hands raw on my shirts, I know what they mean when they say "For richer, for poorer" . . .

I stood out on the sidewalk in front of the radio playhouse and shivered because I had sold my overcoat six weeks before. There was nowhere else to turn to, and I hadn't the gall to go back to Maria so early in the day. Uptown, downtown, crosstown—all the same to me.

A man walked up, looked me over, handed me a slip of paper. It said, "Could you tell me how to get to South Ferry from here?"

I said, "Sure. Take the Seventh Avenue subway—"

He shook his head, pointed to an ear. Deaf. I took the pencil he offered, wrote down the directions. He tipped his hat, went his way. I remember wondering how a guy like that got such a nice warm coat. Some agency, I guessed. I got all my faculties and no overcoat. He's a deaf mute and has an overcoat. I'll take the overcoat.

Then the great idea hit me. I smacked my hands together, whooped like a drunken Indian, and headed at a dead run for the West Side, where Maria was trying to make a home for me out of an eleven-a-month cold water flat. I reached it, flung myself up three flights of stairs, fell gasping and moaning for breath inside the room. Maria didn't know what to make of it, and figured even less when I got wind enough to explain. If she was possessed, I wanted to know, could she keep from tipping anybody off about it *if she wrote the information down?*

"I don't know, Eddie. I never tried it."

"Well, try it, damn it. Try it!"

"H-how?"

I glanced at the ninety-eight cent alarm clock on the stove. "Come on, babe. Get your coat on. We're going to get some money."

She was used to me by this time or she never would have done it. I didn't tell her until we reached the pawnshop that the money was coming from the one thing of value she'd hung onto—the star sapphire I'd given her as an engagement ring the day before we got married. Under the three golden spheres I relieved her of it, shoved an old envelope and a stub of pencil into her hands, and dragged her in.

I knew the broker well by that time. The only Irishman I'd ever seen in a hock shop. "Terry, me lad," I shouted. "I'm about to do you a favor. Hock me this ring for eighty bucks and you can't lose a thing." I gave it to him. He grunted sourly. Maria started forward, about to speak. I shoved her toward a trunk, pointed at the paper and pencil. She grinned and began to write.

"I'll give ye ten," said Terence.

"And I'll take me pathronage ilsewhere," I mocked him.

"Twinty, an' ye're a young thief."

"Sivinty-Foive, ye grave-robber."

"Twinty-two an' a half, and be dommed to ye. It's white gold, not platinum."

"Platinum's twenty bucks an ounce on the open

market you pernicious old Gael, and gold's thirty-
five. Don't blind me with your jeweler's tricks."

And still not an interruption from Maria.

Terence looked at the ring carefully through his
glass.

"Thirty dollars."

"Will you make that thirty-two fifty?"

"I will that, and there I'm done."

"You're a good business man, Terence, and I'll treat
you right. You just went up ten dollars and I can afford
to come down ten. That's meeting you halfway at
sixty-five dollars."

Maria's pencil scribbled busily.

"Fifty dollars to get yez out o' my store," said the
broker with a great effort.

"Fifty-seven fifty."

We settled at fifty-five; I signed the book and we
left. As soon as we were outside I snatched the envelope. Maria had written no less than twelve times,
"Don't be a fool. He only paid sixty for it when it
was new."

I kissed her then and there. "It works," I breathed.
"It works!"

She looked at the envelope. "The truth will out,"
she grinned. "But Eddie—I didn't want to pawn that
ring. I—"

"You dry up and leave it to me, pal," I said. "Come
home—I want you to dig up that dress of yours—you
know, the black-brown one with the truffles on it."

"Ruffles," she said. "You eat truffles. But it's an
evening gown, Eddie. Where—"

"—are we going? West five-two street, babe, and
we're going to scrabble up all the dirt from gutter to
gutter." I stopped in front of a "Tuxedos to Hire"
joint. "I'm going in here. You beat it home and pretty
up."

She did, under protest. I got myself a fair-enough
dinner jacket, and brought it home. In two hours we
looked like a million. I tucked the thin little roll into
my pocket, and we started. We took the subway to
Fiftieth and caught a cab there to go to Fifty-second.
A thirty-cent cab ride looks just as good as a three-

dollar one at the far end of the line. I carried a battery of sharp pencils and Maria had my little black book.

Well, it was a snap, I'd barge into a table, and because I looked it and felt it, the old "friends" thought I was up on top again, and so they were glad to see me. Maria sat quietly with her book in front of her. I told everyone she was gathering material for a novel. Once in a while she would look sharply at a couple of faces and begin to scribble madly. For once in my life I let other people pick up the checks, and we worked practically the whole street. We got out of there with eighteen bucks left, which is something of a record, and I took the lady all the way home in a taxi. We spent the rest of the night poring through the book.

Man! What a haul! There was enough dirt there to resurface the Dust Bowl and ten like it. Advance information on big business deals; messings about with the Stock Exchange; who was seeing who, how long, why, and how much it cost; what book a major studio was going to buy; the truth about that fixed fight at the Garden Monday night. I found Maria an excellent editor. Once the little old *poltergeist* had dissipated, she was quite impersonal about what she found out. We took, out of more than two hundred juicy items, ten that were due to happen within the next twenty-four hours. They were carefully picked to do the least possible harm if they were made public, and they all packed a wallop. There was an act of sabotage, three elopements, a decision on the locale of the premiere of a new picture, two business deals, a diplomatic stroke of genius, a lapse of option on an erstwhile great movie star, and the name and address of a firm which was going to get a government contract for high-pressure boilers on the battlewagons under construction at Boston Navy Yard. I wrote them up, wording them for the most punch, and first thing the next morning I took them up to the newspaper with the largest newsstand circulation in the country. I was in the office for forty minutes, and I walked out with fifty bucks advance. The following day I got a wire to come in and go to work. Every item had come as predicted. Score, one hundred per cent.

So I'm back in the big time again. Yes, I'm the guy they talk about. The one about whom they say, "Did you see his column today? Holy Swiss cheese, where does that man get all his information?" And "I'd like to know how a Broadway columnist gets that radio personality."

Well, I get the first from my wife, who sits quietly, writing in a little black book. She gets her dope from a thousand million little *poltergeisten*. And don't mention radio to me too often. The name of Eddie Gretchen still stinks on the stem, but I don't care. I don't use it any more. You ought to know who I am by this time.

SHADOW, SHADOW ON THE WALL

IT WAS well after bedtime and Bobby was asleep, dreaming of a place with black butterflies that stayed, and a dog with a wuffly nose and blunt, friendly rubber teeth. It was a dark place, and comfy with all the edges blurred and soft, and he could make them all jump if he wanted to.

But then there was a sharp scythe of light that swept everything away (except in the shaded smoothness of the blank wall beside the door: someone *always* lived there) and Mommy Gwen was coming into the room with a blaze of hallway behind her. She clicked the high-up switch, the one he couldn't reach, and room light came cruelly. Mommy Gwen changed from a flat, black, light-rimmed set of cardboard triangles to a night-lit, daytime sort of Mommy Gwen.

Her hair was wide and her chin was narrow. Her shoulders were wide and her waist was narrow. Her hips were wide and her skirt was narrow, and under it all were her two hard silky sticks of legs. Her arms hung down from the wide tips of her shoulders, straight and elbowless when she walked. She never moved her arms when she walked. She never moved them at all unless she wanted to do something with them.

"You're awake." Her voice was hard, wide, flat, pointy too.

"I was asleep," said Bobby.

"Don't contradict. Get up."

Bobby sat up and fisted his eyes. "Is Daddy—"

"Your father is not in the house. He went away. He won't be back for a whole day—maybe two. So there's no use in yelling for him."

"Wasn't going to yell for him, Mommy Gwen."

152

"Very well, then. Get up."

Wondering, Bobby got up. His flannel sleeper pulled at his shoulders and at the soles of his snug-covered feet. He felt tousled.

"Get your toys, Bobby."

"What toys, Mommy Gwen?"

Her voice snapped like wet clothes on the line in a big wind. "Your toys—all of them!"

He went to the playbox and lifted the lid. He stopped, turned, stared at her. Her arms hung straight at her sides, as straight as her two level eyes under the straight shelf of brow. He bent to the playbox. Gollywick, Humptydoodle and the blocks came out; the starry-wormy piece of the old phonograph, the cracked sugar egg with the peephole girl in it, the cardboard kaleido-scope and the magic set with the seven silvery rings that made a trick he couldn't do but Daddy could. He took them all out and put them on the floor.

"Here," said Mommy Gwen. She moved one straight-line arm to point to her feet with one straight-line finger. He picked up the toys and brought them to her, one at a time, two at a time, until they were all there. "Neatly, neatly," she muttered. She bent in the middle like a garage door and did brisk things with the toys, so that the scattered pile of them became a square stack. "Get the rest," she said.

He looked into the playbox and took out the old wood-framed slate and the mixed-up box of crayons; the English annual story book and an old candle, and that was all for the playbox. In the closet were some little boxing-gloves and a tennis racket with broken strings, and an old ukulele with no strings at all. And that was all for the closet. He brought them to her, and she stacked them with the others.

"Those things too," she said, and at last bent her elbow to point around. From the dresser came the two squirrels and a monkey that Daddy had made from pipe cleaners, a small square of plate-glass he had found on Henry Street; a clockwork top that sounded like a church talking, and the broken clock Jerry had left on the porch last week. Bobby brought them all

to Mommy Gwen, every one. "Are you going to put
me in another room?"

"No indeed." Mommy Gwen took up the neat stack
of toys. It was tall in her arms. The top fell off and
thunked on the floor, bounced, chased around in a
tilted circle. "Get it," said Mommy Gwen.

Bobby picked it up and reached it toward her. She
stooped until he could put it on the stack, snug between the tennis racket and the box of crayons.
Mommy Gwen didn't say thank you, but went away
through the door, leaving Bobby standing, staring
after her. He heard her hard feet go down the hall,
heard the bump as she pressed open the guest-room
door with her knee. There was a rattle and click as
she set his toys down on the spare bed, the one without a spread, the one with dusty blue ticking on the
mattress. Then she came back again.

"Why aren't you in bed?" She clapped her hands.
They sounded dry, like sticks breaking. Startled, he
popped back into bed and drew the covers up to his
chin. There used to be someone who had a warm
cheek and a soft word for him when he did that, but
that was a long time ago. He lay with his eyes round
in the light, looking at Mommy Gwen.

"You've been bad," she said. "You broke a
window in the shed and you tracked mud into my
kitchen and you've been noisy and rude. So you'll
stay right here in this room without your toys until I
say you can come out. Do you understand me?"

"Yes," he said. He said quickly, because he remembered in time. "Yes ma'am."

She struck the switch swiftly, without warning, so
that the darkness dazzled him, made him blink. But
right away it was the room again, with the scythe of
light and the shaded something hiding in the top
corner of the wall by the door. There was always
something shifting about there.

She went away then, thumping the door closed,
leaving the darkness and taking away the light, all but
a rug-fuzzed yellow streak under the door. Bobby
looked away from that, and for a moment, for just a
moment, he was inside his shadow-pictures where the

rubber-fanged dog and the fleshy black butterflies stayed. Sometimes they stayed . . . but mostly they were gone as soon as he moved. Or maybe they changed into something else. Anyway, he liked it there, where they all lived, and he wished he could be with them, in the shadow country.

Just before he fell asleep, he saw them moving and shifting in the blank wall by the door. He smiled at them and went to sleep.

When he awoke, it was early. He couldn't smell the coffee from downstairs yet, even. There was a ruddy-yellow sunswatch on the blank wall, a crooked square, just waiting for him. He jumped out of bed and ran to it. He washed his hands in it, squatted down on the floor with his arms out. "Now!" he said.

He locked his thumbs together and slowly flapped his hands. And there on the wall was a black butterfly, flapping its wings right along with him. "Hello, butterfly," said Bobby.

He made it jump. He made it turn and settle to the bottom of the light patch, and fold its wings up and up until they were together. Suddenly he whipped one hand away, peeled back the sleeve of his sleeper, and presto! there was a long-necked duck. "Quack-ack!" said Bobby, and the duck obligingly opened its bill, threw up its head to quack. Bobby made it curl up its bill until it was an eagle. He didn't know what kind of noise an eagle made, so he said "Eagle-eagle-eagle-eagle," and that sounded fine. He laughed.

When he laughed Mommy Gwen slammed the door open and stood there in a straight-lined white bathrobe and straight flat slippers. "What are you playing with?"

Bobby held up his empty hands.

"I was just—"

She took two steps into the room. "Get up," she said. Her lips were pale. Bobby got up, wondering why she was so angry. "I heard you laugh," she said in a hissy kind of whisper. She looked him up and down, looked at the floor around him. "What were you playing with?"

"A eagle," said Bobby.

"A what? Tell me the truth!"

Bobby waved his empty hands vaguely and looked away from her. She had such an angry face.

She stepped, reached, put a hard hand around his wrist. She lifted his arm so high he went on tiptoes, and with her other hand she felt his body, this side, that side. "You're hiding something. What is it? Where is it? What were you playing with?"

"Nothing. Reely, reely truly nothing," gasped Bobby as she shook and patted. She wasn't spanking. She never spanked. She did other things.

"You're being punished," she said in her shrill angry whisper. "Stupid, stupid, stupid . . . too stupid to know you're being punished." She set him down with a thump and went to the door. "Don't let me hear you laugh again. You've been bad, and you're not being kept in this room to enjoy yourself. Now you stay here and think about how bad you are breaking windows. Tracking mud. Lying."

She went out and closed the door with a steadiness that was like slamming, but quiet. Bobby looked at the door and wondered for a moment about that broken window. He'd been terribly sorry; it was just that the golf ball bounced so hard. Daddy had told him he should be more careful, and he had watched sorrowfully while Daddy put in a new pane. Then Daddy had given him a little piece of putty to play with and asked him never to do it again and he'd promised not to. And the whole time Mommy Gwen hadn't said a thing to him about it. She'd just looked at him every once in a while with her eyes and her mouth straight and thin, and she'd waited. She'd waited until Daddy went away.

He went back to his sunbeam and forgot all about Mommy Gwen.

After he'd made another butterfly and a dog's head and an alligator on the wall, the sunbeam got so thin that he couldn't make anything more, except, for a while, little black finger shadows that ran up and down the strip of light like ants on a matchstick. Soon there was no sunbeam at all, so he sat on the edge of his bed and watched the vague flickering of the something that lived in the end wall. It was a *different* kind of something. It wasn't a good something, and it wasn't bad. It just lived there, and the difference between it and the other things, the butterflies and dogs and swans and eagles who lived there, was that the something didn't need his hands to make it be alive. The something—stayed. Some day he was going to make a butterfly or a dog or a horse that would stay after he moved his hands away. Meanwhile, the only one who stayed, the only one who lived all the time in the shadow country, was this something that flickered up there where the two walls met the ceiling. "I'm going right in there and play with you," Bobby told it. "You'll see."

There was a red wagon with three wheels in the yard, and a gnarly tree to be climbed. Jerry came and called for a while, but Mommy Gwen sent him away. *"He's been bad."* So Jerry went away.

Bad bad bad. Funny how the things he did didn't used to be bad before Daddy married Mommy Gwen.

Mommy Gwen didn't want Bobby. That was all right—Bobby didn't want Mommy Gwen either. Daddy sometimes said to grown-up people that Bobby was much better off with someone to care for him. Bobby could remember 'way back when he used to say that with his arm around Mommy Gwen's shoulders and his voice ringing. He could remember when Daddy said it quietly, from the other side of the room, with a voice like an angry "I'm sorry." And now, Daddy hadn't said it at all for a long time.

Bobby sat on the edge of his bed and hummed to himself, thinking these thoughts, and he hummed to himself and didn't think of anything at all. He found a ladybug crawling up the dresser and caught it the careful way, circling it with his thumb and finger so that it crawled up on his hand by itself. Sometimes when you pinched them up they got busted. He stood on the windowsill and hunted until he found the little hole in the screen that the ladybug must have used to come in. He let the bug walk on the screen and guided it to the hole. It flew away, happy.

The room was flooded with warm dull light reflected from the sparkly black shed roof, and he couldn't make any shadow country people at all, so he made them in his head until he felt sleepy. He lay down then and hummed softly to himself until he fell asleep. And through the long afternoon the thing in the wall flickered and shifted and lived.

At dusk Mommy Gwen came back. Bobby may have heard her on the stairs; anyway, when the door opened on the dim room he was sitting up in bed, thumbing his eyes.

The ceiling blazed. "What have you been doing?"

"Was asleep, I guess. Is it night time?"

"Very nearly. I suppose you're hungry." She had a covered dish.

"Mmm."

"What kind of an answer is that?" she snapped.

"Yes ma'am I'm hungry Mommy Gwen," he said rapidly.

"That's a little better. Here." She thrust the dish at him. He took it, removed the top plate and put it under the bowl. Oatmeal. He looked at it, at her.

"Well?"

"Thank you, Mommy Gwen." He began to eat with the teaspoon he had found hilt-deep in the grey-brown mess. There was no sugar on it.

"I suppose you expect me to fetch you some sugar," she said after a time.

"No'm," he said truthfully, and then wondered why her face went all angry and disappointed.

"What have you been doing all day?"

"Nothing. Playin'. Then I was asleep."

"Little sluggard." Suddenly she shouted at him. "What's the matter with you? Are you too stupid to be afraid? Are you too stupid to ask me to let you come downstairs? Are you too stupid to cry? Why don't you cry?"

He stared at her, round-eyed. "You wouldn't let me come down if I ast you," he said wonderingly. "So

I didn't ast." He scooped up some oatmeal. "I don't feel like cryin,' Mommy Gwen, I don't hurt."

"You're bad and you're being punished and it should hurt," she said furiously. She turned off the light with a vicious swipe of her hard straight hand, and went out, slamming the door.

Bobby sat still in the dark and wished he could go into the shadow country, the way he always dreamed he could. He'd go there and play with the butterflies and the fuzz-edged, blunt-toothed dogs and giraffes, and they'd stay and he'd stay and Mommy Gwen would never be able to get in, ever. Except that Daddy wouldn't be able to come with him, or Jerry either, and that would be a shame.

He scrambled quietly out of bed and stood for a moment looking at the wall by the door. He could almost for-sure see the flickering thing that lived there, even in the dark. When there was light on the wall, it flickered a shade darker than the light. At night it flickered a shade lighter than the black. It was always there, and Bobby knew it was alive. He knew it without question, like "my name is Bobby" and "Mommy Gwen doesn't want me."

Quietly, quietly, he tiptoed to the other side of the room where there was a small table lamp. He took it down and laid it carefully on the floor. He pulled the plug out and brought it down under the lower rung of the table so it led straight across the floor to the wall-receptacle, and plugged it in again. Now he could move the lamp quite far out into the room, almost to the middle.

The lamp had a round shade that was open at the top. Lying on its side, the shade pointed its open top at the blank wall by the door. Bobby, with the sureness of long practice, moved in the darkness to his closet and got his dark-red flannel bathrobe from a low hook. He folded it once and draped it over the large lower end of the lamp shade. He pushed the button.

On the shadow country wall appeared a brilliant disk of light, crossed by just the hints of the four wires that held the shade in place. There was a dark spot in the middle where they met.

Bobby looked at it critically. Then, squatting between the lamp and the wall, he put out his hand.

A duck. "Quackle-ackle," he whispered.

An eagle. "Eagle—eagle—eagle—eagle," he said softly.

An alligator. "Bap bap," the alligator went as it opened and closed its long snout.

He withdrew his hands and studied the round, cross-scarred light on the wall. The blurred center shadow and its radiating lines looked a little like a waterbug, the kind that can run on the surface of a brook. It soon dissatisfied him; it just sat there without doing anything. He put his thumb in his mouth and bit it gently until an idea came to him. Then he scrambled to the bed, underneath which he found his slippers. He put one on the floor in front of the lamp, and propped the other toe-upward against it. He regarded the wall gravely for a time, and then lay flat on his stomach on the floor. Watching the shadow carefully, he put his elbows together on the carpet, twined his forearms together and merged the shadow of his hands with the shadow of the slipper.

The result enchanted him. It was something like a spider, and something like a gorilla. It was a brand-new something that no one had ever seen before. He writhed his fingers and then held them still, and now the thing's knobby head had triangular luminous eyes and a jaw that swung, gaping. It had long arms for reaching and a delicate whorl of tentacles. He moved the least little bit, and it wagged its great head and blinked at him. Watching it, he felt suddenly that the flickering thing that lived in the high corner had crept out and down toward the beast he had made, closer and closer to it until—whoosh!—it noiselessly merged with the beast, an act as quick and complete as the marriage of raindrops on a windowpane.

Bobby crowed with delight. "Stay, stay," he begged. "Oh, stay there! I'll pet you! I'll give you good things to eat! Please stay, *please!*"

The thing glowered at him. He thought it would

stay, but he didn't chance moving his hands away just yet.

The door crashed open, the switch clicked, the room filled with an explosion of light.

"What are you doing?"

Bobby lay frozen, his elbows on the carpet in front of him, his forearms together, his hands twisted oddly. He put his chin on his shoulder so he could look at her standing there stiff and menacing: "I was —was just—"

She swooped down on him. She snatched him up off the floor and plumped him down on the bed. She kicked and scattered his slippers. She snatched up the lamp, pulling the cord out of the wall with the motion. "You were not to have any toys," she said in the hissing voice. "That means you were not to make any toys. For this you'll stay in here for—what are you staring at?"

Bobby spread his hands and brought them together ecstatically, holding tight. His eyes sparkled, and his small white teeth peeped out so that they could see what he was smiling at. "He stayed, he did," said Bobby. "He stayed!"

"I don't know what you're talking about and I will not stay here to find out," snapped Mommy Gwen. "I think you're a mental case." She marched to the door, striking the high switch.

The room went dark—except for that blank wall by the door.

Mommy Gwen screamed.

Bobby covered his eyes.

Mommy Gwen screamed again, hoarsely this time. It was a sound like a dog's bark, but drawn out and out.

There was a long silence. Bobby peeped through his fingers at the dimly glowing wall. He took his hands down, sat up straight, drew his knees up to his chest and put his arms around them. "Well!" he said.

Feet pounded up the stairs. "Gwen! Gwen!"

"Hello, Daddy."

Daddy ran in, turning on the light. "Where's

Mommy Gwen, Bob boy? What happened? I heard a—"

Bobby pointed at the wall. "She's in there," he said.

Daddy couldn't have understood him, for he turned and ran out the door calling "Gwen! Gwen!"

Bobby sat still and watched the fading shadow on the wall, quite visible even in the blaze of the overhead light. The shadow was moving, moving. It was a point-down triangle thrust into another point-down triangle which was mounted on a third, and underneath were the two hard sticks of legs. It had its arms up, its shadow-fists clenched, and it pounded and pounded silently on the wall.

"Now I'm never going into the shadow country," said Bobby complacently. *"She's* there."

So he never did.

TWINK

FEELING NUMB, I put the phone down. I've got to get out of here, I thought. I've got to go ask old Frozen Face. I've got to get home.

But there was the old man, just that minute coming out of his office. For the first time, I was glad he'd put my desk out there in front of the golden-oak slab of his door, like a welcome mat. I looked up at him and I guess I looked anxious.

He stopped beside me. "Something wrong?"

I wet my lips, but I couldn't say anything. Stupid! Why shouldn't I be able to say *I've got to get out of here!*

"The kid?"

"Yes," I said. "We have to take her in this afternoon."

"Well, get out of here," he said brusquely.

I stood up, I couldn't look at him. "Thanks."

"Shaddap," he said gruffly. "Call up if you need anything."

"I won't need anything." Except courage. Faith, if you like. And whatever kind of hypocrisy it takes to conceal from a child how scared you are.

I reached for my hat. Old Frozen Face just stood there. I looked back from the outer door and he was still there, staring at the place where I'd been.

I almost yelled at him some explosive, blathering series of syllables that would in some way explain to him that I'm not a freak; look at the creases in my blue pants; look at my shoeshine, just the same as yours; look how my hairline's receding—look, look, I've got heartburn and lumps in my throat!

At the same time, I wanted to yell something else,

something about, yes, you were kind to me because you know what's with me, with my kid; but you can't know how it is. With you, I'm once removed from anything you could feel, like the Hundred Neediest Cases in the newspaper at Christmas. You believe it, sure, but you can't know how it is.

So with one inner voice saying I'm what you are and another saying You can't know how it is, I let them crash together and silence one another, and said nothing, but made the frosted glass door swing shut and walked over to the elevators.

I had to wait and that seemed wrong. I looked at the indicators, and saw that all of the cars were running, and that seemed wrong, too. Everything else ought to stop except one car for me and it ought to be here now! I stood there realizing how irrational all this was, but fuming anyway.

Behind me, I heard *thunk*-pat, *thunk*-pat, and from the corner of my eye saw it was Bernie Pitt on his crutches. I turned very slightly so my back was to him. Bernie is a very nice guy, but I just didn't want to talk to anybody. It was as if talking to somebody would slow up the elevator.

I hoped he hadn't noticed my turning away like that. Then I found I could see his reflection in the polished gray-green marble of the wall by the elevator. He was looking at me; I could see his face tilt as he glanced down at the hat I was twisting in my hands. Then it tipped up and back a little as he studied the tops of the doors, the way a man does when he wants to look as if he's absorbed in his own thoughts. So he's seen that hat, at ten in the morning, and that meant I was going out, and he knew all about me and Twink and the accident, and was being considerate.

Old Frozen Face was being considerate, too. Old Frozen Face always did the correctly considerate thing. Like hiring Bernie, who was a cripple.

I hated myself for thinking that.

It made me hate Bernie. I glared at his reflection. Just then, one of the elevator doors across the corridor rolled open and I jumped and spun.

"Up!" said the operator.

Bernie stumped into it without looking at me. The door closed. I wished I had a rock to throw at it.

I tried hard to get hold of myself. I knew what was happening. Scare a man badly enough, and then make the thing he fears diffuse and unreachable, and he'll lash out indiscriminately at everything and everyone. Well, lash away, boy, I told myself, and get it out of your stinking small-minded system before you get home.

"Down?" the operator asked.

Shouldering into the car, I felt I had a right to be sore at the operator for taking so long. The elevator was full of intruders and the descent took forever, and for a moment I got so mad, I swear I could have hunched my shoulders and sprayed them all with adrenalin. Then the doors opened again and there was the lobby like a part of all outdoors, and the offices upstairs no longer contained or confined me, and their people no longer intruded.

I scurried down the steps and along the concourse to the interurban station, trusting my feet and letting the rest of me fly along with the eager aimlessness of a peace-dove released at a school pageant.

How can there be any unreality in your cosmos? I asked myself. The day Twink goes to the hospital— that's *today*; it's here. It's been a real thing all this time, for all it was in the future; it was more real than most other things in the world. And now it's come and you're walking underwater, seeing through murk.

But the whole world's helping, too. Nothing is so unreal to the commuter as a commuter's station at ten in the morning. The trains, lying in these echoing acres, look like great eviscerated larvae. The funereal train crew, gossiping as if work were done, as if it weren't their job to get me home before the sawbones went to work on my little girl.

I went to them. "Baytown?"

They looked at me, a conductor, a motorman, a platform man. They were different sizes and shapes, but their faces were all the same gray, and contained the same damnable sense of the fitness of things. They were in a place that belonged to them, doing the right thing at the right time in it. They were steady and sober and absolutely at the service of commuters-by-the-ton, but a man outbound at ten in the morning, though tolerable, could hardly be served. He wasn't what they were there for.

I went into the train and sat down and looked at my watch. Four minutes. They were going to make me wait four minutes.

I sat in an empty car and looked at the glare of yellow woven plastic pretending to be rattan, steel panels pretending to be wood, and the advertising signs. There were three kinds of signs: the imperatives, which said Buy and Drink and Use; the comparatives, which said Better, Richer, Finer (and never stated what they were better and richer and finer than); and the nominatives, which stupidly and without explanation proclaimed a name.

I snorted at them all and reached for a paper someone had left on a nearby seat. If its previous owner had been there, I think I'd have punched him right in the mouth. I've always respected books and I've always felt that a paper is a sort of book. This character had put the middle section in upside down, folded some sheets back on themselves and away from the centerline, so that page covers skewed and flopped all around, and he had generally churned up and mutilated the dead white body before discarding it.

Growling, I began to put it back together again.

CHEERFUL TONY WEAKER
Doomed Child Sinking. Gifts
and Cards Pouring In for
Early Birthday

NEW YORK, June 25 (AP)—1973's Child of the Year, five-year-old Tony Marshall, has been placed under oxygen at Memorial Hospital, while a staff of top cancer specialists stand a twenty-four-hour watch at his bedside. Hope that he will live to see his sixth birthday in August has faded.

The boy, whose famous smile made him known

from coast to coast as Cheerful Tony, is suffering
from advanced leukemia.

Angrily I hurled the paper away from me. It came
to pieces in midair and fluttered to the floor, to lie
there accusingly and stare at me. I swore and got up
and gathered it together and crammed it out of sight
on the seat ahead of mine.

"Cheerful Tony," I muttered. Some convolution
of the face muscles, some accident of the dental arch,
a trick of the light and the fortuitous presence of a
news photographer as lucky as the guy who got the
flag-raising at Iwo—put 'em all together and you've
got a national hero. What good did it do to anyone
to read about Cheerful Tony or to write about it?
What good did it do Tony?

For an ugly moment, I wished I could trade places
with Tony's father. All he had to worry about was
cancer—nice, certain cancer—and once it was finished, that would be the end of it.

But I didn't envy him the publicity, and for the
hundred thousandth time, I thanked the Powers that
so few people knew about Twink.

The doors slid shut and the train started. I let go
a sigh of relief and hunched back in my seat, wondering how to make the time go faster. Not the time; the
train. I pushed my feet uselessly against the legs of
the next seat, made a calm and childish calculation
of what I was doing (forty pounds foot-pressure forward, forty pounds shoulder-pressure backward—
equals zero) and sat up feeling like a fool. I began
to look at the ads again.

Imperative, comparative, nominative.

Maybe my technique had been wrong all along.
Maybe I should have used nothing but advertising
tactics on Twink the whole time. After all, those were
tested methods, with more than a century of proof
behind them.

"Relax with oxygen," I should have told her.
"Live," I should have told her, twelve times a minute,
in the best imperative mood. "Live . . . live." And,

"Don't struggle. Let the doctor work. It will be easier." (Than what?) And, of course, the pervasive, in-
stitutional nominative: "Twink. Everybody knows
Twink. Everybody loves Twink." Until she believes it
all. . . .

The anger, which had changed to hysteria, con-
verted itself now into crawling depression. It de-
scended on me like the shadow of some great reptile,
something that moved slowly and implacably and
without human understanding. I felt utterly alone. I
was different. Apart. More apart than Bernie, who
had left half a leg in Formosa. More than Sue
Gaskell, who was the only Negro in the copy department—by God, another "kindness" of old Frozen Face.

Why couldn't someone (besides Twink) share this
with me? Even Doris couldn't. Doris loved me; she
ate with me, slept with me, worried and hoped with
me, but this thing with Twink was something she
couldn't share. She just wasn't equipped for it. Sometimes I wondered how she held still for that. This
might go on for years . . . if Twink lived at all . . .
Twink and I sharing a thing that Doris could never
know, even being Twink's mother.

Suddenly I found someone else to be mad at and
the depression lifted enough to let it in. You guys, I
thought, you helpful people who put welded track on
these roadbeds, who designed pneumatic dampers and
cushioned wheels for the trains—did it ever occur to
you that a man might want something to listen to in
a train in 1973? Twenty years ago, I could have
listened to the wheels and I could have made up a
song to go along with them; *blippety-clak, blippety-
clak.*

Blippety-clink, poor little Twink, don't let her die—
All right, fellows—on second thought, you can have
your welded rails.

"Baytown," said the annunciator in a cultured
voice, and deceleration helped me up out of the seat.

I went to the door and was through it before it had
slid all the way open, shot down the platform while
fumbling for my commuter's plate, missed the scan-
ner slot with it and skinned my knuckles, dropped

the plate, picked it up, got it into the slot, waited forever—well, three seconds—while it scanned, punched
and slid out my receipt.

I was just about to blow a fuse because there was
no taxi, but there was. I couldn't bark my address
because the driver knew it, and I couldn't wave bribes
at him because he was paid by the development, and
anyway his turbines had a governor to keep him from
speeding as fast as I wanted. All I could do was huddle
on the cushion and bite the ball of my thumb.

The house was very quiet. For some reason, I had
expected to find them in the nursery, but there wasn't
a sound from there. I found Doris stretched out on
the settee in the den, looking drowsy.

"Doris!"

"Shh. 'Lo. Twink's asleep."

I ran to her. "Is she . . . do you . . . are you . . ."

She rumpled my hair "Shhh," she said again. "My
goodness, it's going to be all right."

I leaned very close and whispered, "Scared. I'm
scared."

"I'm scared, too," she said reasonably, "but I'm
not going to go all to pieces."

I knelt there, soaking up a kind of strength, a kind
of peace from her. "Sorry, darling. I've been—" I
shuddered. "On the train, I was reading about Cheerful Tony. I was thinking how they'd do the same thing
with us, if they knew."

"Only more." She half-laughed. "All that mail, all
those reporters, newsreel men. All that glory. All that
—noise."

We listened together to the morning silence. It was
the first time since she'd phoned me that I'd noticed
how lovely the day was.

"Thank you," she whispered.

"For what?"

"For not telling them. For being—well, for just
being; I guess that's what I'm trying to say. And for
Twink."

"For *Twink?*"

"Of course. She's my little girl. If it hadn't been for you, I'd never have known her."

"I think the way motherhood makes people crazy is one of the nicest things around," I said.

She answered, but with her eyes. Then she said, "We have to be there at noon."

I looked at my watch, leaped wildly to my feet, turned left, turned right.

Doris openly laughed at me. "How long does it take to get to the hospital?" she asked.

"Well, ten minutes, but we have to . . . don't we have to, uh?"

"No, we don't. We have more than an hour. Sit down and help me be quiet. Want something to eat before we go?"

"No. God, no. Shall I fix—"

"Not for me."

"Oh," Slowly I sat down again.

She giggled. "You're funny."

"Yeah."

"Have any trouble getting away?" She was making talk, I knew, but I went right along with it.

"Matter of fact, no," I said. "Old Frozen Face took one look at me after you called and chased me out."

"He's so wonderful. . . . . Honey! Don't call him that!"

I growled something wordless. "He makes me mad."

"After all he's done?"

"Yes, after all he's done," I said irritably.

Because of all he's done, I think. All my life, I'm a misfit for one reason or another; then, in college, they found out this thing about me and I worked my way through being a laboratory curiosity. I got into the papers. Not too much—just enough to keep me from getting any decent job after I graduated. Except with Frozen Face, of course. I didn't apply; he wrote me. He hired all his people that way. People with half a leg. Blind people in Personnel. Ex-cons who couldn't get started.

At first, it looked as if his people had escaped the things that hung over them—thanks to him. Then,

after a while, you began to realize that you wouldn't
be working there if you didn't have something wrong
with you. It was like starving all your life until you
found you could be well fed and taken care of till the
day you died—in a leprosarium.

But I said, "Sorry, Doris. Just naturally ungrateful,
I guess . . . Twink's waking up."

"Oh, dear! I thought she might sleep until—"

"Shh."

Ever since the accident (I'd turned the car over;
they say you can't do that with any car later than
1970, but I'm the guy), Twink had terrified me every
time she woke up. She'd come out of the normal sleep
of a normal baby and enter a frightening stillness, a
cessation of everything but life itself. It was, I suppose, coma; but I'd lived with seven weeks of it
once, and even now the momentary passage through
it, from sleep to waking, was so loaded with terror and
guilt for me that it was all I could take. And when
you add to that the fact that I had to hide it, that
above all else I had to be strength to her, and comfort,
as she awoke—

Then it was over; she was awake, confused, dimly
happy.

"Hi, baby. How's my Twink?"

Doris, tense on the couch, not breathing, waiting—

"It's all right. Twink's all right," I said.

"Well, of course!"

I shot Doris a look. There wasn't a hairline crack
in that enamel of hers, but it suddenly occurred to
me that it was past time for me to stop using her as
the pillar of strength around here. I bent and kissed
her and said (making it sound like a joke, because I
knew she'd prefer it that way), "Okay, honey; from
here on, you can scream curses."

"I'll just do that," she said gratefully.

Did the accident have anything directly to do with
it or was it just me? Champlain (yes, the Champlain,
who took up where Rhine left off) had a number
of theories about it. The most likely one was that
when my peculiar equipment got stirred up enough in

the crash and for that awful hour afterward, I sent
such a surge of empathy at Twink that I created a
response. You can call it telepathy if you like—Champlain did—but I don't like the sound of that. Of
course, I'm biased. You can take your extrasensoria,
all of them, and—well, just take 'em and leave me be.

It may be that I was better equipped than the next
guy to adjust to this, having lived for some eight
years with the mild notoriety of being the boy who
never scored less than 88 on the Rhine cards. But
personally, constitutionally, I never was meant to be
different from other people. What I mean is that my
useless ability (I don't regard it as a talent and I won't
call it a gift) didn't have to make any difference to
anyone. I could be just as good as a short-order cook,
just as bad a ticket-taker, as anyone else. But I was
never given the chance of living like a human being.

I could stick around the parapsychology laboratories, earning a living like an ape in the zoo (and not
much of a living at that; even in this enlightened era,
there isn't a rich parapsychologist), or I could go out
and get a job. And the way my dark past followed me,
you'd think I was wearing a Flying Saucer for a halo.
"Oh, yes—you're the mind-reading fellow." You know
what that can do to your prospects?

Usually I didn't get the job. Once I was hired,
though, they knew. Twice I landed jobs and they
found out later. Each time there was someone who
went to the boss, seniority and all, and said, "Look,
it's him or me." And guess who got the pink slip.

Would you work every day with somebody who
could read your mind? Who hasn't got secrets? Whose
life really is an open book? I can tell you, I wouldn't
work next to someone like that, yet I'm about as inof-
fensive as they come. And what was driving me out
of my head—and I was two-thirds out when I met
Doris and then Frozen Face—was that everyone
thought I could read minds and I *can't!*

But Doris, who had heard of me even before she
met me, never mentioned it. First she was nice to
be with, and then I had to be with her, and then I
came to a big, fat, soul-searching decision and con-

fessed All to her one night, and she kissed me on the end of the nose and said she'd known about it all along and it didn't matter; and if I said I couldn't read minds but was only good at guessing Rhine cards, why, she believed me; and if I ever did learn to read minds, she wished I'd hurry up and read hers, because she was getting awfully impatient. After that, I'd have married her if she looked like a gila monster. Actually she looked like the Tenniel Alice-in-Wonderland, only with curly hair.

When I came up for breath from that interchange, I liked people a hell of a lot more than I ever had before. I guess that's another way of saying I liked myself some, at last.

Then along came the letter from Frozen Face, and Twink came up, and the accident happened.

And after the accident, the nightmare ability to dip down into the living silence that was Twink now, an unstirring something that couldn't see or speak or hear, something that was dreadfully hurt and just hovering, barely alive. My kid. And after about seven weeks, a movement, a weak tensing. It was the faintest possible echo of fear, and always a retreat from it that shoved the little thing close to dying again. Then there would be the silence again, and the stirring, and the fear and retreat.

Why I tried, how I thought to try, I don't know, but I did what I could each time to reassure her. I would tense till I ached and say, *It's all right, honey, don't be afraid, it's all over now*. And I hoped it helped her, and then I thought it did, and then one night I knew it did, because I saw the tension coming and stopped it, and there was a different kind of silence, like sleeping, not like coma.

After that, she got better fast, and I took hold of the slim hope that she might one day see and run and climb like other kids, hear music, go to school . . .

She had to, she *had* to, or I was a murderer. I was worse than that. Your out-and-out murderer knows what he's doing. More likely than not, he does it to get something, for profit.

But me—want to know what I did?

We'd been out for a drive in our shiny new car—well, it was second-hand, but the newest one I'd ever owned—and I wanted to get a couple of cartons of cigarettes before we crossed the state line, to save—guess!—a few cents tax. It was a six-lane road, three each way. I was in my middle lane.

Doris pointed at a big neon sign. "There's a place!"

I hauled the wheel over and shot straight across the right-hand lane. The truck just nipped the rear fender and over we went.

For six cents. Come to think of it, I never did buy the cigarettes, so I can't even claim that.

There's your superman, "wild talents" and all. A goddam highway boob.

Doris and Twink went to the hospital, bleeding and bleeding, then lying for days, waxy, doll-like, and came out, back to me, saying it wasn't my fault it wasn't my fault . . . God! And Twink as good as dead.

There was a reception committee waiting for us—two big names in medicine, McClintock and Zein—and, of course, Champlain. Busy boy. He wouldn't miss this for the world. But, thank heavens, no press.

"Come on, I want to talk to you," said Champlain, big breezy as ever, looking like the world's least likely suspect as a parapsychologist. I never did like Champlain, but he was the only person in the world besides Doris I could really talk to. At the moment, I wished I hadn't ever talked to him. Especially about Twink. But he knew and that was that.

He muscled me away from Doris and Twink.

"No!" cried Doris, and Twink was frightened.

"Now don't you worry, little lady; he'll be back with you before we do a thing," he called heartily, and there I was going one way and Doris and Twink the other. What could I do?

He pushed me through a door and I had the choice of sitting in a big armchair or falling down, the way he rushed me. He kicked the door shut.

"Here's some medicine." He got a bottle out of

the top desk drawer. "McClintock let me see where
he put it, the fool."

"I don't want any."

"Come on now."

"Get away from me," I said, and meant it. Inside
myself, I turned to admire that tone, harsh and rough
and completely decisive. I'd always thought only movie
gangsters could make a speech like that sound so real.
And while I was backing off from myself, admiring. I
suddenly sobbed and swore and swore and sobbed.
It was pretty disgusting.

"Wow," said Champlain. He put the bottle down
and got some pills. He filled a paper cup with ice-
water and came over to me. "Take these."

"I don't want any."

"You'll take'm or I'll hold your nose and ram 'em
down your neck with a stick!"

I took them and the water. As I keep saying, I'm
no superman. "What are they?"

"Dexamyl. Brighten you up, smooth you down all
at once. Now tell me what's the matter."

I said it, said what I hadn't put in words before.
"Twink's going to die. I want her to."

"The two best specialists in the world say no."

"Let her die! She's going out of here as a basket
case if you don't! I know. I know better'n anybody.
Blind. Deaf. Paralyzed. All she can do is sort of flop.
Let her die!"

"Don't be so goddamn selfish."

A kick in the face would have shocked me a good
deal less. I just gawked at him.

"Sure, selfish," he repeated. "You pulled a little
bobble that anybody might have done and your wife
won't blame you for it. To you, it's become a big, important bobble because you never were involved in
anything important before. The only way you can prove
it's important is to suffer an important punishment.
The worst thing you can think of is to have Twink
dead. The next worse is to have her go through life
the way she is now. You want one of those things."

I called him something.

"Sure I am," he agreed. "Absolutely. In the eyes

of the guy who's wrong, the guy who's right is always just what you said."

I used another one.

"That, too," he said, and beamed.

I put up my hands and let them fall. "What do you want me to do? What are you picking on me for?"

He came over and sat sideways on the broad arm of the chair. "I want you to get in there and help us. Help Twink."

"I'd be in the way."

He hit me on the shoulderblade. It was done as a sort of friendly gesture, but it was done hard. "You can get through to her, can't you?"

"Yes."

"She's been hurt. Badly. This is going to hurt her, too—a whole lot. She may not want to go through with it."

"She has a choice?"

"Every patient has a choice. Other things being equal, they live or they don't. If they've been hurt and they see more pain coming, they might not want to go through with it."

"I still don't see how I—"

"Would you like to keep wondering whether you could have saved her life?"

"She's going to die, anyway."

He got up and stood in front of me with his big fists on his hips, glaring at me silently until I had to raise my face. He held me with his eyes until I couldn't stand it and then he said, rough and gentle like a tiger purring, "You damn near killed her once and now you want to finish the job. That it?"

"All right, all *right!*" I shouted. "I'll do *anything!*"

"Good!" And suddenly he dropped on one knee and took both of my hands in both of his. It was a very surprising thing for him to do and strangely effective. I could feel currents of his immense vitality from those big hands; it was as if my ego, wrinkled like a prune, was swelling up sleek and healthy.

He said, softly and with deep earnestness, "All you've got to do is make her want to live. You've got to be with her and wait for her and help her along and keep her convinced that no matter what happens, no matter how it hurts, it's worth it because she's going to live."

"All right," I whispered.

"She's only a little girl. She takes things just the way she finds them and she doesn't make allowances. If something looks like fear to her, or anger, it is that. If something looks like love, or wisdom, or strength, that's just how she'll take it. Be strong and wise for her."

"Me?"

He got up. "You." He went to the desk and got the bottle and poured a paper cup full. He held it out to me.

I wiped my eyes with the backs of my hands and stood up. "No thanks. I don't need it," I told him.

He twitched his eyebrows and drank the liquor himself and we went out.

They put me through the scrub room just as if I'd been a surgeon—gloves, mask and all—and then we went into the operating theater. Doris was already there, all fixed up, too. I went and kissed her right through the mask and she smiled.

I said, "You look lovely in white," and wondered where that had come from; and, "Hi-i, Twink."

Somewhere in the blindness, in the confines of paralysis, there was a shadow of fear and, down inside that, a warm little response. And the fear evaporated. I looked up and met Champlain's eyes. That unnatural feeling under my mask was, to my complete astonishment, a grin. I nodded and he winked back and said, "I guess you can go ahead, Mac."

Now listen, Twink, I said with all my heart, I love you and I'm here, I'm right here with you no matter what happens. Something's going to happen, something big, and it's going to change everything for you. Some of it won't be . . . won't be nice. But they have to do it. For you, Twink. Even when it isn't nice, it's for you. You've got to let them. You've got to help them. They love you, but I love you most of all. You mustn't go away. If it hurts you too much, you just tell me and I'll make them stop.

Then something was the matter, very much the matter. Shaken, I crowded close and tried to see what McClintock was doing. "Back off a little," he growled.

"Back off, my eyeball. What the hell are you winding around her head?"

Champlain barked at me, "Cut it out! The one thing you don't get is angry!"

Doris made a little sound. I spun to her. She was smiling. No, she wasn't. Her eyes were all screwed up. A tear came out.

"Doris!"

Her face relaxed instantly, as if the nerves had been cut. Then she opened her eyes and looked at me. "I'm all right," she said.

There was a calling, a calling, a calling.

All right, Twink, I'm here. I didn't go away. I'm right here, honey. If you want them to stop, you just say so.

A pause, then a tremulous questioning.

Yes, yes, I said, I'm here. Every single second. I'm not going away. Again the pause and then, like a flicker of light, a hot, glad little response.

Doris moaned, almost a whisper. I shot a glance at her, then at Champlain.

"You want that stopped?" he asked.

"No," I said. "I promised her she could."

Doris' hand moved. I took it. It was wet. She squeezed mine, hard.

Something from Twink, unlike anything I had ever experienced before. Except the accident. Yes, it was like the accident—and *stop!* STOP!

"Stop!" I gasped. "Stop it!"

McClintock went right on working as if I hadn't made a sound. The other specialist, Zein, said to Champlain as if I couldn't hear, "Do we have to stand for this?"

"You're damn right you do," said Champlain.

Working, McClintock asked, "Stop? What do you mean, stop?"

Zein mumbled something to him. McClintock

nodded and a nurse came flying across the room with a tray of hypodermics. McClintock used a number of them.

Twink went quiet. For a moment, I thought I would faint from relief.

All right, honey? All right? I made them stop. Twinkie. Is it all right?

Twink!

Twink!

I made some sort of noise, I don't know what. Champlain's hands were on my shoulders, grinding down like two oversized C-clamps. I shrugged off one, knocked off the other with my wrist. "Twink!" I shouted. Then Doris screamed shrilly and Twink vibrated like a gong.

"That won't do," I snapped, gesturing with my head.

"Want her out?"

"Don't you dare," said Doris.

"Yes. Now."

McClintock began, "Who's—? but Champlain said, "Shut up. Take her out."

After that, it went very quickly.

Just a little more, Twink, and it'll be all over and you'll be warm and comfy and you can sleep. And I'll be near while you sleep and with you when you wake up.

I tried to stop McClintock once more, when he took the little arm that had been immobilized across Twink's chest for so long and twisted it brutally up and back. But this time Champlain was on McClintock's side and he was right; the pain stopped almost instantly.

And then—was it weeks later, hours? The biggest part was over and they did things to her eyes, her mouth, while I found ways and yet new ways to thrust aside fury, ignore fatigue, negate fear, and press on and on and around and inside with I love you, Twink; I'm here; it's all right. Just a little more, a little—there, it's stopped. Are you all right, Twink?

She was all right. She was wonderful. When they were through with her, she was weak and she looked like hell, but she was all right. I stared at her and stared at her and I couldn't believe it; I couldn't contain it, either. I didn't know what to do. So I began to laugh.

"Okay, let's get out of here." Champlain loomed over me like a grounded parachute.

"Yeah, wait." I sidled around him and went to McClintock. "Thanks," I said. "I'm sorry."

"It's okay," he said tonelessly.

Zein just turned his back.

I sat by the bed where they had put Doris, tired, and I waited.

This was a lot different from that other hospital, that other time. Then I'd committed something and I was full of fear. Now I'd accomplished something and I was full of hope—and liquor, but they tasted much the same. Twink was asleep, breathing beautiful even breaths, far too weary to be afraid.

I was glad about so many things and I mentally thumbed through them all, one by one, with a huge and quiet delight. And I think that the one I was happiest about was my saying to Champlain afterward, "She'd have been perfectly all right even if I hadn't been there."

What I was so pleased about was that I said it, I didn't ask it. And he had laughed and filled my cup again.

"You're a mind-reader," he said, and it was the first time I had ever heard that and thought it was funny.

"You wanted a case history of a human being born with little or no birth trauma, you son."

"Well, nobody ever had one before," he admitted. "I'd have had a lot less trouble in my young life if my dad had been able to paddle me down that particular canal in a canoe."

"You're a louse and it was worth it," I told him.

Doris turned her head impatiently.

"I'm here," I whispered.

She looked at me out of the same composed, porcelain face. "Hi. How's your girl friend?"

"My *other* girl friend. Doris, she's beautiful! All pink. She has two eyes. Ten toes. Eight fingers."

"What?"

"And two thumbs. She's all right, darling, really all right. A perfectly normal newborn girl-baby."

"Oh, I'm . . . so glad. Does she . . . can you still—even after the Caesarean?"

I nodded and in that split second, I wished my fool head had rolled right off. Because as I did it, I realized that I could have lied; she *wanted* me to.

She began to cry. She said, "You made them knock me out and you did it all yourself. You've had her to talk to all this time and you always will, as long as you both live. I'll never ever cry about this again, I promise, because it's not your fault and I love you, anyway. But I'm going to cry about it now."

I crouched with my head on her pillow for a long, long time. Then I went away, because she was nowhere near finished.

She's never cried about that since, though.

Never once.

I guess there's some way a man can make up a thing like that to a woman.

If he keeps looking.

I guess.